ILLUSTRATED LIBRARY OF NATURE

AN ENCYCLOPEDIA OF NATURAL HISTORY ENCOMPASSING
ALL ASPECTS OF NATURE AND WILDLIFE
PREVIOUSLY PUBLISHED AS
LIFE NATURE LIBRARY

VOLUME
2
BIRDS

1984 EDITION

H. S. STUTTMAN INC. PUBLISHERS • WESTPORT, CONNECTICUT 06889

© 1980 Time-Life Books Inc. All rights reserved.
No part of this book may be reproduced in any form or by any electronic or mechanical means, including information storage and retrieval devices or systems, without prior written permission from the publisher, except that brief passages may be quoted for reviews.

2P(679)45-57

Contents

1	From Archaeopteryx to Sparrow	9
2	What It Takes to Fly	33
3	Birds as Food Gatherers	57
4	How Many Birds?	79
5	The Riddle of Migration	99
6	How Birds Communicate	119
7	From Egg to Adult	137
8	Toward a Balance with Man	165
	Bibliography	186
	Credits	187
	Index	188

About the Author

Roger Tory Peterson's first ambition was to be a painter of birds, but feeling that he could not make a living at that, he went to art school in the hope of succeeding as a commercial artist. Birds, however, remained his passion. While teaching natural history and art, he painted birds when he could. He eventually was able to persuade a publisher to put out a bird guide that was filled with his illustrations and that introduced a new system of field identification. This system is now known, wherever birds are studied, as the Peterson system. It has revolutionized bird watching and made its inventor the best-known ornithologist in the world. The first Peterson *Field Guide*, which was devoted to birds of America, was followed by others on a dozen different countries. All together, his books have sold more than eight million copies.

This extraordinary success has enabled the man who "could not make a living painting birds" to travel all over the globe, observing his favorite creatures. Along the way he has written and lectured widely and has been an officer of 18 leading ornithological organizations. He has been awarded the Brewster Medal of the American Ornithologists' Union, the John Burroughs Medal, the Geoffrey St. Hilaire Gold Medal (France), the Linne Medal of the Swedish Royal Academy of Sciences, the Gold Medal of the Explorer's Club, medals from the New York Zoological Society, the National Audubon Society and the World Wildlife Fund and awards from a dozen other organizations. He has received honorary degrees in science and the humanities from eight universities.

EARLIEST KNOWN BIRD, *Archaeopteryx* left its semireptilian print in clay. It had feathers, but probably it was a poor flier, spending much time on the ground. Wing claws helped it clamber about in trees.

1
From Archaeopteryx to Sparrow

WHAT manner of creatures are birds? Certainly, of all the higher forms of life, the vertebrates, or backboned animals, they are the most beautiful, most melodious, most admired, most studied—and most defended. They far outnumber all other vertebrates except fishes and can be found virtually everywhere throughout the world, from the edges of the polar icecaps and the highest Himalayan and Andean slopes to the roughest seas, the darkest jungles, the most barren deserts and the most crowded cities. The center of the Antarctic continent is the only place on the world's surface where birds have not been found. Some even invade the fishes' environment to a depth of 750 feet (229 m) or more, while others hide in caves so dark that they must employ a sort of built-in sonar to find their way about.

Nearly a century ago T. H. Huxley called birds "glorified reptiles." This term may grate harshly on the ears of gentle souls who keep parakeets or feed cardinals at the window, but there is much to support Huxley's contention. Birds share many characteristics with reptiles—certain skeletal and muscular features, similar eggs, an "egg tooth" on the upper jaw at hatching time, to name just a few. But the unique feature that sets them apart from all other

FOUR FOSSIL BIRDS

ICHTHYORNIS

After 50 million years birds had come a long way from the reptilian Archaeopteryx. Ichthyornis was the size of a pigeon, probably looked somewhat like a modern tern and had teeth. It lived on the shores of North America's inland sea 90 million years ago and was probably a skillful flier, but had small, weak legs.

HESPERORNIS

Hesperornis also lived 90 million years ago on America's inland sea. It resembled a modern loon, with legs set far back. A strong swimmer, it had only rudimentary wings and was not able to fly. Sharp reptilian teeth lined its beak. Several Hesperornis species evolved, the largest of them the size of a small seal.

animals is that they have feathers. All birds have feathers, and no other creatures possess them.

Considering the fact that life on earth extends back into the spectrum of time for more than two billion years, birds are a latter-day creation. Paleontologists believe that they began to branch off from reptilian stock sometime about 150 million years ago, shortly after the first mammals.

The oldest known bird in the fossil record dates back to the late Jurassic Period, about 135 million years ago, and although there must have been still earlier birds or subbirds, this one has a dramatic significance all its own. It was found in limestone in Solenhofen, Bavaria, in 1861, and would have been classified as a reptile except for the unmistakable imprint of feathers. The discovery was a scientific bombshell. Only two years before, in 1859, Charles Darwin had published his then-controversial work, *On the Origin of Species*—and here was beautifully imprinted proof of his new theory, a missing link from the past: evidence that birds had evolved from reptiles. The fossil was named *Archaeopteryx,* meaning "ancient wing." In 1877 a second skeleton was discovered about 10 miles (16 km) away and in 1956 a third was found.

A LTHOUGH not quite a bird in the modern mold, *Archaeopteryx* was certainly not a true reptile. Its head, however, was lizard-like, with toothed jaws, its slender tail with many movable vertebrae was skeletally like that of a reptile, and its wing bones terminated in three slender, unfused, clawed fingers. Still, it had *feathers*.

Archaeopteryx probably did not fly easily. If we rationalize from its appearance, we might assume that it ran over the ground on strong legs and clambered up rocks, shrubs and trees with the assistance of its clawed wing-fingers. Its rounded wings and long but rather wide tail suggest that it was a glider that launched itself only for short distances, like a flying squirrel. It is perfectly clear, from studying its anatomy, that it could not have flown very well. We can easily imagine the predicament which led to the fossilization of the three individuals so long ago. They were probably forced into reluctant flight by some pursuing reptilian predator, only to flop down on the water and mud from which they could not rise.

To this day, *Archaeopteryx lithographica*, which was about the size of a crow, remains the only known species representing the subclass archaeornithes, or "ancestral birds," and we can only guess at the type of reptile from which it descended. This may have been one of the thecodonts, the possessor of long hind limbs on which it ran semierect, using its long tail as a balance.

Concurrently, also during the Jurassic, another reptilian experiment in flight resulted in the pterodactyls, which flew on slender batlike wings of skin. Though these creatures developed certain birdlike features such as beaks and lightweight, pneumatic bones, they were not destined to survive. The Cretaceous Period, which began about 135 million years ago and ended roughly 70 million years ago, saw their proliferation and also their demise, and witnessed the rise of the "true birds."

These were the neornithes, birds such as *Hesperornis*, a toothed diver resembling a flightless loon four or five feet (1.2 to 1.5 m) long, and *Ichthyornis*, a tern-like sea bird. Their remains were found in the Cretaceous shales of Kansas. A cormorant-like bird also lived during this period and a primitive flamingo has been found in Scandinavia, so it is obvious that water birds had already diverged widely in form and adaptation by this time. The current era is often called the Age of Mammals, as distinct from the Age of Reptiles, which drew to a close with the exit of the dinosaurs and pterosaurs. The early part of this era, the Paleocene and Eocene, 70 to 40 million years ago, was a time of great development that saw the ascendancy of the birds over the reptiles. Many of the modern orders of birds emerged—including an ancestral ostrich and primitive pelicans, herons, ducks, birds of prey, fowl-like birds, shore birds, owls, cranes and others. As we advance further, through the Oligocene and Miocene, 40 to 10 million years ago, we find many modern genera appearing, birds very similar to present-day forms.

A modern bird watcher, stepping backward in time about 20 million years to scan a Miocene lake with his binoculars, would spot many familiar-looking individuals but none that he could match precisely with those of today. But there also existed certain other birds that were in blind alleys, for example, the phorusrhacids, huge flightless birds with massive heads nearly as large as those of horses. These fearsome fowl left no modern descendants. This was the period when birds enjoyed their greatest variety. Pierce Brodkorb, of the University of Florida, estimated that about 10,750 species were living contemporaneously, nearly a fifth more than exist today. During the Pliocene, 10 to 2 million years ago, many species emerged that fly on earth today—species that can claim antiquity far greater than that of man.

The Pleistocene, lasting one or two million years, when man was slowly coming into his own, was a time of pressure and extermination. The world was playing hot and cold with living things, alternating between glaciation and benign interglacial periods. The great ice sheets eliminated many plants, and the birds scattered accordingly.

Today the number of species of birds on earth is usually estimated to be about 9,000. The total number of now-extinct species described from fossil evidence is in the neighborhood of 1,000.

Actually, any paleontologist will point out that this figure does not give even a remotely accurate picture of the number of species that have existed on earth during the last 140 million years. Birds, with their fragile, hollow bones, do not lend themselves as well to fossilization as do the mollusks with their hard shells or the mammals and large reptiles with their relatively solid bones. The road from *Archaeopteryx* to modern birds is paved with genesis and extinction. Species have arisen, have had their day and have faded away or given rise to new forms that were better adapted to the new conditions of a changing world. Brodkorb, drawing on his knowledge of fossil history, came up with a tentative, overall figure of 154,000 bird species, past and present. The living birds made up only 17 per cent of this total. The other species have followed *Archaeopteryx* into the void.

The biologist often speaks of "adaptive radiation." This means, in the evolutionary sense, that the descendants of a single species of animal may adapt to a number of new environments or modes of life. By so doing, they "radiate," changing in form and structure away from the ancestral type to a number of divergent types.

Adaptive radiation was strikingly revealed to Darwin when his research vessel, the *Beagle*, anchored at the Galápagos Islands 600 miles (970 km) off the coast of Ecuador in 1835. Here he found a complex group of small, dark, finchlike birds now known as the Geospizinae. They were similar enough to be recognizable as a group that had presumably descended from a single source, perhaps some

DIATRYMA

A 60-million-year-old flightless giant of the North American plains, this bird stood seven feet (2.1 m) tall and had a head as large as that of a horse. Its sharp bill and powerful legs suggest that it was a predator that lived by running down small reptiles and mammals, in much the same way as the secretary bird does today.

PHORUSRHACOS

Related to Diatryma and with a similar predatory bill and rudimentary wings, Phorusrhacos was somewhat smaller— about as tall as a man. It lived in South America 25 million years ago, unhindered by the large predatory mammals that later emerged there. The modern cranelike cariama of South America may be akin to it.

FROM ARCHAEOPTERYX TO SPARROW

EARTHBOUND REPTILE TO AIRBORNE BIRD

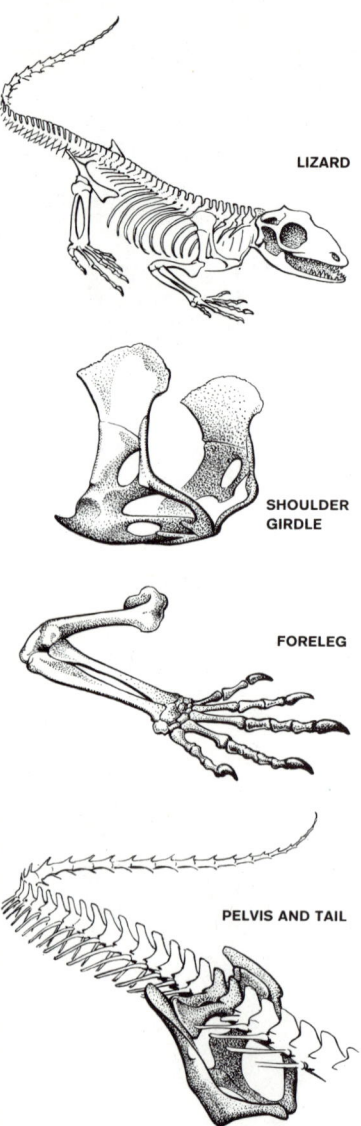

Although descended from the same reptilian ancestors, lizards and birds have diverged considerably in structure. A typical lizard today has a long backbone and an even longer tail. Its solid frame and stout limbs, with many movable bones, are well suited to its four-footed gait.

Its shoulder girdle is strong, made of three heavy bones, but the breastbone is shallow, since large chest muscles are not needed by lizards. Short sprawling forelegs give the lizard a built-in crouch, but it uses an ankle of many elements and a five-toed foot to run swiftly. The pivot point of body weight is the pelvis. Up to 100 tail vertebrae provide rear balance.

seedeating ground finch carried by the wind to these remote islands. Perhaps a small flock made the sea passage together. Surviving, these first wind-borne immigrants found no other small birds to offer competition. Environmental niches were empty, so eventually the colonists, prospering and increasing, adapted to various modes of existence. When Darwin made his historic visit he found that some Geospizinines were seedeaters as their ancestors are presumed to have been, but that others fed on insects, still others on cactus and one form even filled the role of a woodpecker. Their bills varied from thin, warbler-like bills to very thick beaks like those of grosbeaks. They had, in fact, evolved so as to exploit virtually every feeding opportunity the islands offered to small birds.

When we discuss Galápagos finches we are talking about relatively recent radiation. Consider the extraordinary radiation from *Archaeopteryx* to the bewildering array of modern birds.

Evolution is a fluid process which can be represented by a two-dimensional family tree, but more accurately it is three-dimensional, with many twigs and branches dying off while others, reaching out in all directions, continue to modify and grow. The 9,000 species of birds on earth today represent growing twig ends. They are separate entities, populations that for one reason or another normally do not or cannot interbreed with each other. They are reproductively isolated. This large galaxy of living species has been arranged by systematists into 27 living orders of birds and these in turn have been broken down into some 160 families.

No one ornithologist has ever seen all the world's species in life—or even all of the families, except possibly in zoos. In fact, few are familiar in life with every order. For it is indeed an amazing diversity that exists in the world's population of birds, from the fragile hummingbird weighing less than a penny to the ponderous ostrich weighing more than 300 pounds (136 kg).

Several of the lower orders of birds cannot fly—the ostriches, the rheas, the cassowaries and emus, the kiwis and the penguins. This gave rise to a theory that modern birds did not all come from a common ancestor, but represented two lines of descent—one that had long ago attained flight and one that is not yet off the ground. Those who held this view theorized that the ostriches and other ratites (flightless, running birds with no keel on the breastbone), as well as the penguins, never had been able to fly and were still evolving their wings. However, this view has now been written off and it is accepted that these flightless birds did have flying ancestors but lost the use of their wings because flight was no longer useful to their mode of life. In fact, flight becomes impossible for creatures as ponderous as the ratites, birds large and heavy enough to fill the niche of grazing animals.

Although the ostrich, with its heavily muscled bare thighs, is the largest living bird, even larger species were seen by primitive man not many centuries ago. These were the moas (*Dinornis*) of New Zealand and the elephant birds (*Aepyornis*) of Madagascar. The largest of the moas, like a huge pinheaded ostrich, stood 12 feet (3.7 m) tall and is estimated to have weighed 520 pounds (236 kg). Moa "graveyards" containing hundreds of skeletons have been found in New Zealand and certain of the smaller moas were still numerous a thousand years ago when New Zealand's first settlers arrived. There is evidence that one species existed in the South Island into the 18th Century.

Less is known about the elephant birds, which some like to speculate were Marco Polo's rocs. They were even more heavily built than moas and may have weighed as much as half a ton (454 kg). Whether man destroyed the last of the elephant birds and, if so, how recently, is not known. Early travelers to Madagascar described *Aepyornis* eggs which were used as flasks by natives. A few such flasks are still in existence and they hold two gallons (7.6 l) of liquid.

The ostrich, the giant among living birds, attains a stature of eight feet (2.4 m). It lives like a grazing animal, roaming in little parties over the African savanna in the company of zebras, wildebeests and gazelles. It has the distinction of being the only bird with two toes, one much reduced in size, suggesting that this fleet-footed monster, which can run as fast as 35 miles per hour (56 km/h), is on its way to acquiring a one-toed foot like the horse.

The two rheas are superficially like their African counterpart, but they have three toes and feathered thighs. Nevertheless, as they race across the pampas, they give much the same effect as small ostriches.

Australia also has its ratites, or ostrich-like birds—the emus and the cassowaries. They lack the ostrich's plumage, and they have even more rudimentary wings and a hairy, almost shaggy look. Australian farmers dislike the fast, 120-pound (54-kg) emu because it damages fences and raids crops. Less often seen are the related, forest-dwelling black cassowaries of northern Australia and New Guinea. Papuan natives have a cautious respect for these temperamental birds that have been known to disembowel men with quick slashes from the long, dagger-like nails of their inner toes.

The strangest and perhaps most primitive of all the ratites are the kiwis of New Zealand. Certainly they are the most unbirdlike of all birds, shmoolike creatures shaped like large, hairy footballs and practically devoid of external wings. They have whiskery faces and nostrils placed at the very tips of their long beaks, the better to locate worms during their nocturnal forays. The kiwi's enormous five-inch (13-cm) egg weighs nearly a pound (0.45 kg), one fourth to one third of the bird's body weight. Contrast this with the six- to eight-inch (15- to 20-cm) ostrich egg, which weighs only one sixtieth as much as the female!

From Mexico southward throughout most of the South American continent live the tinamous—chunky, almost tailless birds that lay deeply colored eggs so glossy that they look like porcelain. These ground birds with the haunting, whistled cries look strikingly like partridges, but are not even distantly related to them. Evolution often results in unrelated birds looking rather similar, especially when they fit a similar environment—a phenomenon called convergence, the opposite of adaptive radiation. Tinamous are low in the family tree of living birds, supposedly close to the flightless ratites, but they still possess the ability to fly.

The torpedo-shaped loons and the smaller, lobe-footed grebes are both foot-propelled divers with feet placed far back toward the tail. At first glance they would seem to belong to the same order. Actually, they are quite unrelated, coming from different ancestral lines—another example of convergence.

Penguins cannot fly, yet they have a strongly keeled breastbone and powerful flight muscles. Here, the wings have evolved into flippers, and penguins literally fly through the water, using their fleshy feet as rudders. Because their upright posture, waddling gait, stiff flippers and frock coats present a lovable caricature of *Homo sapiens*, penguins have always appealed to humans. All but one of some 20 living species inhabit cold Southern Hemisphere seas.

Oddly enough, the flightless penguins may have evolved from the same ancestral stock as the albatrosses, the supreme masters of flight. Students point

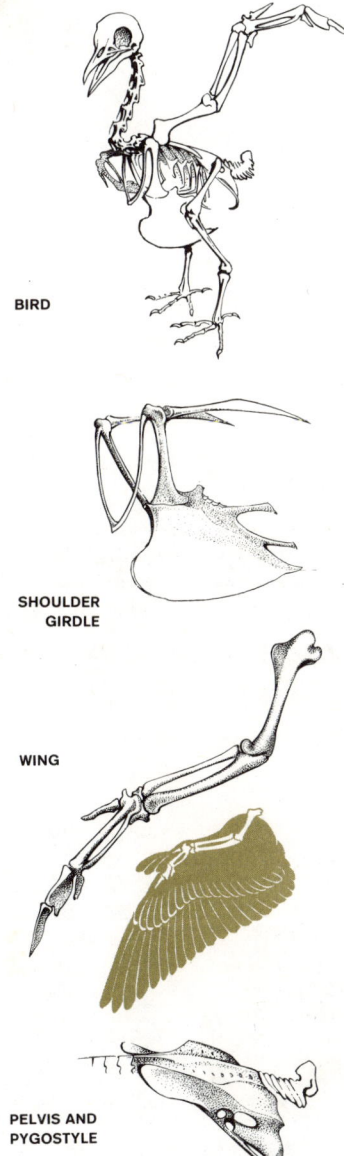

BIRD

SHOULDER GIRDLE

WING

PELVIS AND PYGOSTYLE

Compared to a lizard, a bird is a lightweight flying machine of few skeletal parts. Body bones flattened and welded onto a short backbone support the wings.

The collarbones are fused into a single "wishbone." The breastbone has a deep keel to provide a surface for attachment of large flying muscles. The wing is a lengthened forelimb. As shown in color, the arm carries the short flight feathers. The wrist and three-fingered hand together support the long primaries. The pelvic bones and lower backbone form a rigid unit. The tail feathers are anchored in the muscles surrounding the pygostyle, a fused vestige of the tail of the lizard.

THE GEOLOGIC TIME SCALE

For many years experts have argued about the dates to be assigned to the eras, periods and epochs of the geologic time scale. The scale generally accepted for many years has been based on one devised by J. Laurence Kulp of Columbia University. More recently a scale compiled for the Elsevier Scientific Publishing Company has gained wide acceptance. The scale used in this book is an updated Kulp scale; its relationship to the Elsevier scale is shown in the table below.

DATE
(MILLIONS OF YEARS AGO)

	Kulp Scale	Elsevier Scale
Paleozoic Era		
Cambrian Period	600	570
Ordovician Period	500	500
Silurian Period	440	435
Devonian Period	400	395
Carboniferous Period		
Mississippian Epoch	350	345
Pennsylvanian Epoch	325	310
Permian Period	270	280
Mesozoic Era		
Triassic Period	225	230
Jurassic Period	180	195
Cretaceous Period	135	141
Cenozoic Era		
Tertiary Period		
Paleocene Epoch	70	65
Eocene Epoch	60	55
Oligocene Epoch	40	35
Miocene Epoch	25	22.5
Pliocene Epoch	10	5
Quaternary Period		
Pleistocene Epoch	2	1.8

out that they have in common a beak made up of horny plates, quite unlike the simple sheathlike bills of most other birds. Eons of evolution have made one an avian submarine, the other a sailplane.

Albatrosses, petrels and shearwaters all belong to the order of "tube-nosed swimmers," so called because the nostrils, unlike those of most other birds, are in short tubes on the sides or on the top of the bill. They are the blue-water seaman's companions and range in size from the swallow-sized black-and-white storm-petrels to the wandering albatross, whose wings span more than 11 feet (3.4 m). Although they roam all oceans, the majority of species live in the Southern Hemisphere and are especially numerous between the antarctic ice pack and the southern tips of the other continents.

The word albatross was an English corruption of *alcatraz*, the name the Portuguese seaman applied to all large sea birds, especially pelicans. Pelicans, however, are not closely related to albatrosses; they belong to the next great order of birds, the "totipalmate swimmers," which differ from all other web-footed birds by having the hind toe joined to the front three by a web. They also have throat pouches, relatively small in the boobies, cormorants, anhingas and frigate birds, but enormous in the pelicans—some of them have a pouch capacity of nearly three gallons (11.4 l). All birds of this order are fisheaters; most are marine.

MODERN birds, adapting and changing during the last 100 million years, have filled virtually every available niche in the world. About 120 living species of "long-legged waders" have evolved. These birds—the herons, storks, ibises and related birds with stiltlike legs for stalking the shallows and long compensating necks—make their living catching small fish, frogs and other forms of aquatic life. Bills take a variety of shapes—dagger-like or spearlike, upturned, downturned, shoelike and even spoonlike.

The most specialized of all the wading birds are the colorful flamingos. For years it was unclear which bird family flamingos were most closely related to. They superficially resembled storks, but had gooselike cries and gooselike young. Finally, in the 1970s, C. G. Sibley of Yale University proved from study of their cell chemistry that flamingos were related to storks. Certainly they are unique among birds, with their exaggerated necks and legs and thick, bent, fringed bills to strain food from the mud in which they wade.

The waterfowl, the familiar web-footed swimmers which form the sportsman's game, include the ducks, geese and swans. The distinctive feature that most of the 150 or so species have in common is a flattish "duck" bill, although the mergansers, or fish ducks, are equipped with sawlike mandibles. Some ducks dabble, others dive for a living, while swans, with necks longer than their bodies, dip or tip up for their diet of aquatic plants. Geese, shorter necked, also do this but primarily graze on land for grass and roots.

Among the most spectacular of all groups are the birds of prey. Superbly designed for their predatory task, they are powerful fliers, capable of effortless soaring or plunging bursts of speed. This order has nearly 300 living species. All have hooked beaks for tearing flesh; those that take living prey characteristically have strongly hooked talons. Vultures, those naked-headed birds of prey that feed on carrion, have weaker feet—an obvious adaptation, since their prey cannot escape. Owls, though birds of prey, are not included in this order; more will be said about them later.

The fowl-like birds, approximately 270 living species, include the grouse, turkeys, quails, partridges, pheasants, curassows, guans and mound builders.

They are sturdy ground birds, with grubbing bills and stout, scratching toes. Some are among the world's most gorgeous birds; others, notably the domestic fowl, are among the most economically important.

The cranes, rails, coots, bustards and related families, more than 200 species, belong to an order that we might call marsh birds. The stately cranes are storklike; the rails and coots are more like hens and hide in the reeds. The bustards are heavy-bodied walking birds of treeless plains. All are birds of ancient lineage; some may be losing the fight for survival.

The shore birds, gulls and auks form another order, also united because of internal anatomical similarities. The birds of this multifarious assemblage numbering more than 300 species are highly gregarious and are to be found more widely throughout the world than any other group. The shore birds are small to medium-sized waders that flock along the margins of waterways and the ocean. The gulls and terns are graceful aerialists. Auks fit the same niche in northern seas that penguins do in the Southern Hemisphere, but have not lost their power of flight. Indeed, they have double-purpose wings, which enable them to fly through the air and under the water as well.

Four fifths of the world's living birds are made up of the various orders of land birds, which seem to have had their greatest development in recent geological time. The worldwide pigeons, for example, and the Old World sandgrouse, with their small-headed, short-legged look, total more than 300 living species. They are the only birds able to suck up water when drinking; all other species have to tip their heads up to let the water flow down their throats.

The gaudy parrots, which come in all the colors of the rainbow, are big-headed with deep, hooked beaks and dexterous, prehensile feet. Living for the most part throughout the tropics, they number some 350 living species. Similar to them anatomically but quite different in shape are the worldwide cuckoos and the touracos of Africa, slim-bodied birds with long tails. Their feet, with two toes forward and two aft, as in the parrots, lack dexterity. If we lump the cuckoos and touracos, the order has about 150 species.

Owls were once classified with the hawks because of their hooked beaks and curved talons, but they are actually unrelated to those predatory birds. Rather they furnish another good example of convergent evolution, birds of separate origin developing similar features because of their way of life. Owls take over the night shift from the day-flying hawks and are best characterized by their loose feathering, large heads and large, forward-facing eyes framed by round facial disks. They are found nearly everywhere in the world and number about 150 species.

Another order of nocturnal birds, the goatsuckers, possess fluffy owl-like plumage, but their beaks and feet have degenerated into insignificance. They are flying insect traps, capturing their quarry in cavernous gaping mouths. The whippoorwill and the nighthawk are the best-known North American examples of this group, which numbers more than 100 species.

The most aerial of birds are the swifts, saber-winged, swallow-like birds that spend all their active hours in the open sky. As in the goatsuckers, beaks and feet have atrophied to near uselessness. Most systematists lump the swifts in

THE LONG AND SHORT OF HUMMINGBIRD BILLS

Although nobody knows what the earliest hummingbird bills were like, experts suspect that their dimensions were generally much the same as the bill of the hermit, since most modern hummingbirds' bills are similar to it. However, others have diverged in remarkable ways. The sicklebill's has the most extreme curve of any species, the thornbill's is shortest, and the swordbill's, at five inches (13 cm), is longest. Each is especially adapted for feeding from flowers of a particular size and shape.

the same order as the hummingbirds, pointing out that they branched off the same stem. The gemlike, needle-billed hummers, which include the tiniest of all birds, number well over 300 species and are all found in the New World. No Old World group has matched them at the delicate art of nectar feeding.

The layman is puzzled when he reviews the orders of birds. Why are ostriches, rheas and emus put into separate orders when they look so much alike? And why are loons and grebes in separate orders—or hawks and owls? On the other hand, birds as dissimilar as sandpipers and puffins are placed in the same order. So are cranes and coots. All of this becomes even more puzzling when one looks at the orders of land birds.

Systematists find that the superficial appearance of birds may be deceiving. Unrelated birds may look similar because of a similar way of life—evolution has decreed it so, and they have converged. On the other hand, birds may look very different yet have come from the same ancestral stock; they have diverged. For this reason, specialists usually base their decisions as to the major groups on internal anatomy—the skeleton, the musculature, the palate structure or the anatomy of the foot indicate more accurately their common ancestry. Today even more precise evaluation of relationships can be made by comparing analyses of the birds' heredity-controlling DNA molecules.

Thus the colies, or mousebirds, a small group of six African birds with crests and slender tails, have been put in an order of their own, based partly on their curious foot structure. So have the brightly colored tropical trogons, which are among the world's most beautiful birds.

The kingfishers and their allies are another great order of fantastic variety, classified by their peculiar feet, which are "syndactyl," having the front toes joined for part of their length. The kingfishers with their spearlike bills are nearly worldwide. Other gaudily colored families belonging to this order are the tiny, chubby todies of the West Indies; the motmots of the American tropics that pluck the barbs of their own tail feathers so that the tips look like tennis rackets; the handsome bee-eaters, the rollers and the hoopoes of the Old World; and the huge, bizarre hornbills of the Old World tropics. All of about 200 species nest in holes, usually in banks of earth or in trees.

The woodpeckers and their allies, numbering nearly 400 species, are also hole nesters and include such dissimilar families as the barbets with their whiskery bills, the iridescent jacamars and the huge-billed toucans. The toucans make up for the lack of hornbills in the New World tropics.

CONDENSED as this brief review has been, it still gives an idea of the great variety of the orders. None, however, can compare with the passerines, or perching birds. This order is by far the largest; it contains more than 5,000 species, which have been divided into about 60 families. They range in size and beauty from tiny wrens to large, gorgeous birds of paradise and lyrebirds. This galaxy, three fifths of all the world's birds, has developed most strongly in relatively recent times. In an epoch when such ancient types as the ostriches, pelicans, cranes and others are on the way out, the passerines may well inherit the earth, or that fragment of it that man spares for them.

Although many systematists today regard the finches and sparrows as the most "evolved" of all the perching birds, the older ornithologists put the crows and jays at the top of the family tree. Perhaps they were right; certainly these resourceful birds are plastic, relatively unspecialized, opportunistic and probably capable of much further evolution—and that is what counts.

HOW THE WHITE TERN GETS ITS NAME

Classification is the sorting out of the different kinds of plants and animals into increasingly narrow categories: kingdom, phylum, class, order, family, genus and species. This process, which gives a special scientific name to every living thing, has many uses. For example, the bird on the cover of this book is sometimes called the white tern and sometimes the fairy tern in English. In other languages it has other names. But its scientific name, "Gygis alba," is an unmistakable label the world over and eliminates all confusion. Here is how the white tern is classified and its name derived:

KINGDOM: ANIMAL *(as distinct from plant)*

PHYLUM: CHORDATA *(animals with a dorsal supporting rod, the notochord. In most adult chordates, it is replaced by a backbone; these are the vertebrates)*

CLASS: AVES *(Latin for birds. Excludes other vertebrates like mammals and fishes)*

ORDER: CHARADRIIFORMES *(from a Greek word meaning birds that live in ravines or cliffs. Includes gulls, terns, auks, plovers)*

FAMILY: LARIDAE *(from the Greek word for gull. Includes gulls and terns)*

GENUS: GYGIS *(Greek for a water bird. Includes one group of terns only)*

SPECIES: (GYGIS) ALBA *(Latin for white)*

In short: "Gygis alba," the white tern, with only the generic and specific names being used for its designation.

THE HORNED GREBE, A LOBE-FOOTED MARSH DWELLER, BELONGS TO A PRIMITIVE BIRD ORDER LITTLE CHANGED IN SOME 70 MILLION YEARS

The Living Birds

Descended 135 million years ago from reptilian stock similar to that which produced the dinosaurs, birds have radiated explosively over the earth. They show a wide variety of sizes, shapes, colors and habits. They live in every continent and occupy almost every conceivable niche. Some even nest underground. Together there are over 9,000 living species, plus a few dozen yet to be discovered.

The 27 Orders

Every one of the living species of birds—the count is debated, but in 1975 the consensus was 9,016—is assigned by ornithologists to one of 158 families in 27 major groups or orders (those numbers are disputed too). Many of the birds in a single order may seem wildly unrelated, but they have skeletal or other features that, to trained scientific eyes, relate them unmistakably. The list below opens with the most primitive orders and ends with the most advanced. The figures for families and species are totals from the *Reference List of the Birds of the World*, distributed in the Department of Ornithology, American Museum of Natural History. These figures reflect the far greater diversity of the smaller birds, particularly the songbirds, as compared with the larger, more primitive birds.

ORDER	LIVING FAMILIES	LIVING SPECIES
Sphenisciformes: penguins	1	18
Struthioniformes: ostriches	1	1
Casuariiformes: cassowaries, emus	2	5
Apterygiformes: kiwis	1	3
Rheiformes: rheas	1	2
Tinamiformes: tinamous	1	47
Gaviiformes: loons	1	5
Podicipediformes: grebes	1	19
Procellariiformes: albatrosses, fulmars, petrels	4	104
Pelecaniformes: tropic birds, pelicans, boobies, cormorants, anhingas, frigate birds	6	62
Ciconiiformes: herons, storks, flamingos, etc.	6	122
Anseriformes: screamers, swans, geese, ducks	2	150
Falconiformes: vultures, hawks, eagles, etc.	5	287
Galliformes: grouse, quails, turkeys, etc.	4	270
Gruiformes: cranes, rails, coots, bustards, etc.	12	209
Charadriiformes: jacanas, plovers, sandpipers, stilts, gulls, terns, auks, etc.	16	333
Columbiformes: sandgrouse, pigeons	3	324
Psittaciformes: parrots, parakeets, cockatoos, lories, lorikeets, macaws, lovebirds	3	344
Cuculiformes: touracos, cuckoos	2	149
Strigiformes: owls	2	146
Caprimulgiformes: frogmouths, nightjars	4	103
Apodiformes: swifts, hummingbirds	3	423
Coliiformes: mousebirds	1	6
Trogoniformes: trogons	1	37
Coraciiformes: kingfishers, todies, motmots, bee-eaters, rollers, hoopoes, hornbills	10	198
Piciformes: barbets, honey guides, puffbirds, jacamars, toucans, woodpeckers	6	383
Passeriformes: flycatchers, larks, swallows, wrens, thrushes, warblers, sparrows, etc.	59	5266
TOTALS	158	9016

Red-footed Booby

One of the Pelecaniformes, an ancient order of fisheaters that includes the pelicans and cormorants, this bird nests on bushes and shows little fear of man. It has the long beak, large wings and short legs of the order, as well as webs between all four toes of each foot — the group's unique feature.

Mute Swan

Rearing in the water, a mute swan shows the dense plumage and broad, flat bill of the Anseriformes—the swans, geese, ducks and their relatives. A wild European species brought to the United States as an ornamental park bird, it has spread extensively in the northeastern states.

American Goshawk

This skillful predator, built for quick maneuvering, takes grouse and rabbits. Like most other Falconiformes—the hawks and eagles—it has strong wings, a hooked bill, sharp talons and keen eyesight. The carrion-eating vultures also belong to this order but lack the clutching talons.

Red Jungle Fowl

The progenitor of all domestic chickens, the red jungle fowl of Southeast Asia is grouped with such other fowl-like birds as grouse, pheasants and turkeys in the order of Galliformes. These are scratching birds, with strong feet and breast meat that is, as man well knows, white and succulent.

European Coot

A marsh bird, the European coot has lobed toes that work like rubber fins when it swims. Coots are related to cranes, rails and their allies, and classified as Gruiformes. This order shows wide diversity but has recently lost — and is losing — more species than any other major order.

Royal Tern

Erupting from a South Carolina colony, royal terns fill the sky with flailing wings. Terns are closely related to the gulls and black skimmers and belong with them to the order Charadriiformes, along with auks, puffins, skuas and a host of wading shore birds ranging from sandpipers and plovers to stately avocets. Its members are found throughout the world, even including the arctic and the edge of Antarctica. The Charadriiformes are traditionally associated with the sea, beaches, marshes and salt meadows, but many of them are found inland, hundreds of miles from the ocean. Most of them are strong fliers, and some are the most remarkable migrators known. The golden plover, which is about the size of a robin and does not light on the water to rest, can fly nonstop 2,400 miles (3,900 km) from eastern Canada to South America and arrives with only a two-ounce (57-g) weight loss.

Victoria Crowned Pigeon

One of the biggest pigeons, this 26-inch (66-cm) crested species belongs to the Columbiformes, to which the extinct dodo also belonged. The Columbiformes drink by sucking up water, instead of tilting their heads back to swallow.

Rainbow Lorikeet

Brilliant plumage, a hooked beak and a distinctive toe arrangement—two in front and two in back—place the rainbow lorikeet among the ranks of such birds as parrots, macaws and budgerigars in the Psittaciformes.

White-cheeked Touraco

Colorful and noisy, the African touracos
are classified with the cuckoos as Cuculiformes.
Forest birds with strong claws, they climb
about the trees searching for fruit and insects.

Hoopoe

A long-beaked male hoopoe brings a meal to its waiting family. Like such other Coraciiformes as kingfishers, hornbills and bee-eaters, hoopoes nest in cavities. Possibly because of their foul nesting habits and the fact that a musty odor exudes from the female's preen gland, hoopoes, whose flesh is edible, are among the proscribed foods of the Old Testament.

Tawny Frogmouth

Nocturnal, as are most of the Caprimulgiformes, the tawny frogmouth has its own method of catching insects: Eschewing flying prey it flutters down on creeping things. This order also contains the insect-catching potoos, nightjars, whippoorwills, nighthawks and the noninsectivorous oilbird.

Starling

The aggressive, extremely adaptable common starling, shown here in white-tipped fall plumage, is but one of the more than 5,000 species in the Passeriformes, which is the biggest and perhaps most highly evolved of the 27 bird orders. The passerines, or perching birds, got started only 60 million years ago—in contrast to the water birds, which go back 130 million years—and they are found on every continent except one, Antarctica. They are land birds, small to medium in size, with the raven and lyrebird among the largest. Because of their recent, rapid radiation, the differences between the families tend to be less well-defined than those in other orders and thus a family tree is more difficult to draw. Europeans usually place the intelligent crows and jays on the uppermost branch but, for anatomical reasons, most American experts give top place to such seedeaters as sparrows and finches.

IN BLURRING FLIGHT a group of terns suggests the supreme mobility of birds. Graceful fliers, terns are noted for their migrations. One species, the arctic tern, flies 10,000 miles (16,000 km) to its winter ground.

2

What It Takes to Fly

More than anything else, the feather is responsible for the fact that birds can fly. Flight itself is not unique among animals—most insects fly and one order of mammals, the bats, has developed true flight. Even man, through that extension of himself, the machine, now flies. But the feather is unique and has enabled birds to become unquestionably the most efficient aeronauts of all.

The feather is a marvel of natural engineering. It is at once extremely light and structurally strong, much more versatile than the stretched skin on which a bat supports itself in flight or the rigid structure of an aircraft's wing—and far more readily repaired or replaced when damaged.

Examine the cut-off quill feather of a pigeon. Though nearly weightless it has strength. The stiff shaft of the quill provides rigidity where support is needed, yet it is supple toward its tip, where flexibility is required for split-second aerial maneuvering. Feel the sleekness of the web, soft yet firm. Separate the barbs; zipper them together again by running them through the fingertips as a bird would preen with its bill. The intricacy of the design that allows this can be appreciated by putting the feather under a microscope. It will be seen that each parallel barb, slanting diagonally from the shaft, is not hairlike, but appears as a

FEATHERS FOR FLYING

A bird's flight feather consists of a central shaft with a series of parallel barbs extending diagonally out from it on each side. The barbs in turn have smaller filaments sticking out from them. Equipped with hooks, these tiny filaments lock into a mesh, providing the flight surface that the bird needs to push against the air.

miniature replica of the feather itself, with numerous smaller side branches, or barbules, that overlap those of the neighboring barbs in a herringbone pattern. These in turn have tiny projections called barbicels, many of which are equipped with minute hooks that neatly hold everything in place. The single pigeon feather under scrutiny may have several hundred thousand barbules and millions of barbicels and hooklets.

How did this structural marvel evolve? It takes no great stretch of imagination to envisage a feather as a modified scale, basically like that of a reptile—a longish scale loosely attached, whose outer edges frayed and spread out until it evolved into the highly complex structure that it is today. In fact, birds still wear scales very much like those of reptiles on their feet and legs. And today the scales on the bare shanks of the bald eagle develop from germ buds quite like those which produce the feathers adorning the shanks of the golden eagle. Both are products of the skin, hornified growths as devoid of feeling as our hair or our nails.

The contour feathers are those which give the bird its outward form. Each is built up of a shaft flanked on each side by a web or vane. Clustered around the bases of the contour feathers are the filoplumes, weak, hairlike shafts with a tuft of short barbs at the tip. These are the "hairs" that the housewife singes from a plucked chicken. On many birds there are also down feathers, soft shaftless tufts hidden under the sheath of contour feathers. Powder-down feathers are found in a few groups of birds. Constantly disintegrating into a fine powder, they are used by herons and bitterns to dress their plumage.

It is obvious that feathers contribute more than the gift of flight to birds. As an extremely light, tough, durable padding they also protect the bird's thin and sensitive skin and act as an efficient air conditioner, trapping body heat in the spaces between the fluffed feathers when the temperature is cold, transmitting it through flatly pressed feathers to the outside when it is warm. Nor must we forget the other functions of feathers in the form of crests, beards, plumes and other avian haberdashery.

How many feathers does a bird have? It is an old poser—but actually the contour feathers on a bird have been counted many times. A basic rule seems to be, not surprisingly, that the larger the bird the more numerous its feathers. A dairyman, to settle an argument, once counted all the feathers on a Plymouth Rock hen. There were 8,325. Another investigator, patiently plucking a whistling swan, amassed a record of 25,216 feathers, 80 per cent of which came from the head and the extremely long neck. A ruby-throated hummingbird examined by Alexander Wetmore of the Smithsonian Institution showed a low count of 940, yet the tiny bird had many more feathers per unit of body surface than did the swan. Songbirds run between 1,100 and 4,600 feathers, depending on the species, and the counts are remarkably consistent for any one species, although there is often a seasonal difference. Three house sparrows, for instance, taken in winter, averaged somewhat more than 3,550 feathers, whereas two July specimens, in lighter summer garb, had about 400 fewer apiece. A goldfinch may have as many as 1,000 more feathers on its body in winter than it has in summer.

A structure as intricate as a feather, tough as it may be, is not immune to wear. It frays and may even break. Therefore most grown birds renew their cloaks completely at least once a year, usually in late summer after nesting season. Many birds also have a second complete or partial molt in the spring before the nesting season begins, when they may acquire the full finery which plays a part in aggressive display and courtship.

Feathers are not shed simultaneously, except in penguins and the female hornbill. Nor is it a random process. Flight feathers and tail feathers are usually discarded in pairs, one from the right side and its opposite number on the left, while the replacements emerge. The bird may lack the support of some flight feathers while molting but it is never inhibited in flying. Only ducks, geese and certain other water birds that are not so dependent on their wings for getting food are ever completely flightless in the molting period.

After birds branched off from the reptilian family tree most of the modifications in their skeletal structure became directed toward the airborne life. Their bones became hollow, like dry macaroni, and some of the larger bones even evolved internal struts for reinforcement. Since flight demands a rigid air frame, the body box—the rib cage and especially the backbone—became rigid, with some of the bones fused. Only the many-vertebraed neck and tail remained flexible. A keel evolved on the breastbone for the attachment of the huge flight muscles, which may account for 15 to 25 per cent of a bird's weight, or even, in the case of some hummingbirds, 30 per cent. The pectoral muscles of a human, by comparison, are less than 1 per cent of his total weight.

Lightness is essential to flight. A bird has not only a pair of small lungs that lie against the ribs, but also a marvelous system of air sacs that extend in a most intricate way into virtually every important part of the body and even lead to air spaces in some of the hollow bones. These delicate sacs with the texture of bubbles enable a bird to use the air it breathes much more efficiently than even a mammal with its relatively larger lungs. The air sacs also act as a thermostatic device, for birds with their rapid metabolism and high body temperatures have no cooling sweat glands.

Superb eyesight is another prerequisite of flight. Certainly no other living things can match the birds in one aspect of sight: sharpness. A vulture soaring a mile (1.6 km) above the earth patiently looking for carrion, a hawk cruising over a meadow in search of a mouse, a warbler gleaning insect eggs under leaves or a loon pursuing under-water prey—all are endowed with an extraordinary ability to pick out objects a man would miss. A kestrel searching out its prey relies on eyes eight times better for this task than a man's.

The eye of a bird is very large by mammalian standards. The exposed cornea, which is the only visible part, is small in comparison to the huge eyeball, which rests almost immovably in its bony socket. In most birds the eyes actually bulk larger than the brain. The eye of an eagle or a large owl may be as large as a man's, and the eyeball of an ostrich measures two inches (5.1 cm) across, nearly the diameter of a tennis ball.

Not only can birds see distant things with greater clarity than we do; some can also see more clearly at much closer range. A warbler, constantly on the alert for distant danger in the form of a hawk, can instantly bring its focus to bear on the most minute insect egg an inch (2.5 cm) from its beak, activating strong ciliary muscles which squeeze the rather flat lens into a more spherical shape for close-up vision.

In addition to having a built-in telescope and magnifying glass in the same instrument, most birds are also favored with both monocular and binocular vision. Unlike ours, their eyes are not on the same plane in front (except in owls), but on each side of the head. This gives each eye a great field of monocular vision

THE HAWK'S KEEN EYE

RETINAL IMAGE: MAN

RETINAL IMAGE: HAWK

Hawks see distant objects better than humans do, not because they have "telescopic" vision, as some people believe, but because the retinas of their eyes are more densely packed with visual cells—as many as 1.5 million at their most sensitive points, the foveae. The corresponding spot in a man's eye, the macular area, has only 200,000 such cells. This gives the hawk roughly an eight-to-one advantage, illustrated here by two pictures of a rabbit—one simulating how a small, distant image is crudely received by the retina of a man's eye and the other showing how the image is screened in much greater detail by the hawk's keen eye. Man sees the rabbit only as a blur, but to the hawk, the animal is instantly and easily recognizable.

The pecten, a pleated object furnishing extra blood to the hawk's eye, may help the bird detect distant movements.

VISUAL ADAPTATIONS

In nearly all birds, the left eye's field of vision overlaps the right. This overlapping area provides binocular sight (color), helpful in judging distance and size.

OWL

With both eyes facing forward in a relatively flat face, owls have a wider range of binocular vision than any other bird. Binocular sight is vital to hawks and owls because they hunt lively prey. To see to the side or rear, they just turn their heads.

SPARROW

Songbirds like this white-crowned sparrow have eyes set more to the sides of their heads. They feed on seeds and insects and need some forward binocular vision, but they must at the same time be able to see far to the side to avoid predators.

WOODCOCK

The woodcock needs little forward binocular vision since it feeds by probing in the mud with a flexible bill. Its eyes are set far to the rear, enabling it to see in a complete circle without moving its head and providing some overlap to the rear.

to the side. An American robin cocking its head as it pauses on the lawn is not "listening" for a worm; it is bringing the area of the most acute vision to bear on that side, the better to detect the movement or glint of a worm.

Straight ahead, where the two monocular fields of vision overlap to form a single image, birds also have a field of binocular vision. Optically they thus have the best of two worlds. The woodcock, however, with its long flexible-tipped bill, has little need for binocular vision in front while probing with its sensitive bill for unseen worms; its problem is to spot danger from behind or above while its bill is in the grip of the soil. For this reason its eyes are placed a bit farther back and a bit higher than those of other birds, resulting in binocular vision to the rear and above as well as a relatively narrow binocular field to the front. It can, in truth, "see from the back of its head" and enjoys a full 360° of vision. So does a duck, although it apparently has a narrower field of binocular overlap behind.

The large eyes of owls, placed on the front of the face like those of man, are primarily binocular. Designed for hunting at dusk or in the dark, these wondrous lenses, not set in flattened eyeballs as in most other birds but in deep horny tubes, might be compared to big, wide-apertured lenses mounted on miniature cameras with a relatively small film surface. If the retina, or "film surface," were in the same proportion to the huge lenses as it is in other birds, there would not be room enough to accommodate the eyeballs.

The owl's restricted view to the side makes some small species very easy to capture. One can quite easily catch the little saw-whet owl, for instance, by wiggling one's fingers three feet (0.9 m) before its face to fix its attention, the while slyly grabbing the bird from behind with the other hand.

Owls not only lack the sweep of monocular vision that most birds have, but their eyes are even more nearly immovably fitted in their sockets. This rigid eye structure is compensated for by quick reflex neck movements and very flexible vertebrae. Unable to see out of the corners of their eyes, owls are constantly moving their heads, and can turn them more than a half circle in either direction. This neck-twisting habit often creates the illusion of turning a full circle, and accounts for the ancient superstition that owls can be made to wring their own necks. Many a boy has tried to do this by walking around and around an owl's roosting tree. But when the halfway point is reached, quick as a wink, the head pivots back to the other side, resuming its steadfast stare. And speaking of winking, owls are the only birds that drop the upper lid when blinking, which makes them look astonishingly human. But when they sleep they raise the lower lid as other birds do. All birds also have a third eyelid, the nictitans, a transparent membrane which, by blinking, keeps the eye moist and at the same time allows them to see.

THE bird with perhaps the most myopic vision is the flightless kiwi of New Zealand, which hunts for worms in the dark, apparently by smell. With its nostrils so conveniently located at the tip of its long, thin bill, the kiwi has little need for eyes, and experiments with buckets of sand have shown that this flightless roly-poly can effectively sniff out its food, quickly digging into those pails in which worms were buried and ignoring the others.

Most birds do not have a strongly developed sense of smell nor do they need it. The main exceptions are among the ground-dwelling species such as the kiwi, ducks and snipes, and two water birds, petrels and shearwaters, which react to the smell of cod-liver oil. But ornithologists still argue whether vultures find carrion by sight or by its odor. In 1835 Audubon and John Bachman experimented by hiding some putrid carcasses and exposing others—from the results they concluded that these dark-winged undertakers are guided by sight alone. Nearly a century later, Frank M. Chapman challenged this. At Barro Colorado Island in the Panama Canal he first hid dead mammals in a shed and under burlap. As soon as the carcasses had decayed enough to produce a strong odor, turkey vultures were attracted to the spot and found them. Some critics, not convinced, pointed out that flies and other insects might have betrayed the concealed carcasses. However, when decaying fish with an equally strong odor was hidden, no birds appeared. Chapman concluded that they may have been attracted by one kind of odor and not by another. They were, he thought, finding their food not only by sight, but also by a discriminating use of smell. Kenneth Stager, Curator of Birds at the Los Angeles County Museum, has subsequently discovered that the area of the brain controlling the sense of smell is three times larger in the turkey vulture than the black vulture, strengthening the conjecture that some vultures may, in fact, have better senses of smell than others.

The head of a bird, divested of its feathers and skin, seems to be all beak and eyeballs. For the sake of lightness, the bones that make up the skull are fragile, the brain case is small, teeth have been sacrificed. But the beak is important, for it must act as a hand; with it the bird catches things, picks things up and manipulates them in a most expert manner. It may also act as a tool—a hammer or chisel, pincers, tweezers, pruning shears, nutcracker, hook, spear, strainer or even (in pelicans) a market basket. With their beaks birds also dress their plumage, communicate, weave their nests, minister to the needs of their young, kill their prey and defend themselves. It is as though they did all these things with their lips, for that is roughly what beaks are—modified lips, hardened epidermis, forming a horny sheath over the bony projections of the jaws.

In most birds the bill is beautifully designed for its specific job. Consider the efficient meat-tearing hook of a hawk, the elaborate mud-straining apparatus of a flamingo or a spoonbill, the sensitive probing bill of a woodcock, the powerful seed-cracking pincers of a parrot. By contrast, there are the grotesque beaks of the tropical toucans and hornbills, huge and colorful, seemingly so unwieldy that one marvels that the birds can sustain them in flight. Actually, they are almost as light as sponge rubber, honeycombed with air chambers. But just what the survival value is of these exaggerated adornments we do not know.

The bills of birds may be a clue to their relationships, but not always. Herons, terns, loons and kingfishers, for instance, all have similar spearlike bills, though they are not even remotely related. But they do all spend their lives catching fish, and their bills are another example of convergence. Utterly dissimilar, on the other hand, were the bills of the male and female huia of New Zealand, a wattled, crowlike bird. The male had a stout straight bill for chiseling into dead wood; the female, a slender curved bill for extracting the grubs. Together they hunted on the forest floor in perfect cooperation, probably unique among birds. However, the huia is now extinct, having been wiped out for its feathers.

The feet of birds are as diverse as their bills. Running, perching, wading, scratching and grasping are but some of the more obvious functions of avian feet. Herons have a toothed comb on the center toe with which to scratch themselves and preen. Their slender, widely spaced toes keep them from sinking too deeply into the soft muck; but no heron can match the grotesque length of a

TOE-LOCKING MECHANISM

The bulky muscles of a bird's upper leg are attached to tendons (color) running the length of the lower leg and extending to the ends of the toes. When the bird stands or walks on the ground, these tendons are relaxed (above) and the toes spread out. A bird perching on a branch, however, ordinarily squats and bends its legs (below). This pulls the tendons taut over the joints and draws in the long, slender toes, which become so tightly locked that it can sleep without falling off its perch.

FUNCTION FORMS THE FOOT

OSPREY

This is a typical predator's foot, better for gripping than for walking. The talons tighten reflexively when grasping prey.

WOODPECKER

To help them hold on as they peck at trees, these birds have two toes at the back to act as braces. Most birds have only one.

MALLARD DUCK

A   B   C

HORNED GREBE

Here are two kinds of feet for swimming. The mallard's foot (top) is webbed. The grebe (below) has paddle-like toes (A) for pushing against the water. On the return stroke they fold backward (B, front view; C, side view) to minimize friction.

WHAT IT TAKES TO FLY

jacana's toes, which enable it to trot lightly over floating lily pads. Larks and pipits, which spend most of their time on the ground, have greatly exaggerated hind toenails which act as braces and keep them from rocking back on their heels when the prairie winds blow. Some of the grouse sprout little appendages on the sides of their toes in the fall of the year and by the time the snow flies they have a very useful set of home-grown snowshoes.

Some birds use their feet as hands. A chickadee cracking a sunflower seed holds it firmly with its foot while it hammers it open. A hawk grips its prey while it tears the flesh away with its beak. Parrots are particularly dexterous, some being right-handed, others left-handed.

Most birds that swim—ducks, geese, loons, cormorants, gannets, gulls and albatrosses—are web-footed, while some, such as coots and phalaropes, have flaps or lobes along the sides of their toes. The grebes, often called hell-divers because of their extraordinary submarine abilities, have the most efficient paddles of all, placed so far back that they seem to sprout from the nearly nonexistent tail. Not only do the toes have wide flanges on each side but even the shanks and the nails are flattened to form propeller blades.

Some birds use their feet for attack or defense. The spurs on domestic fowl and pheasants are well known. A kick from the thick two-toed foot of an enraged ostrich is said to be more potent than that of a horse. But probably the most lethal weapons of all are those of the cassowaries, long, knife-blade nails on their inner toes with which they slash each other in combat.

Just as the bills of swifts have degenerated, so have their feet, which are weak and tiny. Since swifts are all wings and mouth, feet are almost unnecessary in their aerial way of life except when they come home to roost. Whippoorwills, nighthawks, swallows and hummingbirds also have diminutive feet and find it difficult to walk—in fact, hummingbirds find it almost impossible.

T HE question is often raised how a perching bird can relax in its sleep without falling off a branch. The answer is that the feet have a built-in locking device: flexor muscles and the tendons that run the full length of the leg and automatically pull the toes into a fist when the bird crouches. The deeply curved "meathooks" of birds of prey operate in much the same way. When a hawk or an owl strikes, its legs bend under the weight of the impact and its talons automatically clutch deep into the vitals of its victim.

At first glance it would appear as though the knee of a bird bends in the opposite direction of ours—backward, not forward. But what most people call the "knee," the visible joint below the feathers, is really the heel. The real knee, the fleshy end of the "drumstick," is concealed by the feathers of the body. So is the entire thighbone, or femur, which is embedded in heavy muscles in a rigid forward-directed position. This distributes the weight in such a way as to give the bird in flight a better center of balance, closer to the powerful flight muscles. The long bare shank of a bird, the tarsometatarsus, is actually the same basic structure which, in humans, is made up of the metatarsal bones which form the arch of the foot. Thus a bird, in our terms, walks on its toes with its heels in the air, in somewhat the same way as we go up on our toes when running to pick up speed.

The shape of a bird's wing is beautifully adapted for flight, thick and blunt along the leading edge, narrower and more bladelike on the trailing edge. Its flat or slightly concave underside and more rounded upper surface act together to create lift in a flow of air. Except when gliding or soaring, however, only the basal half of a bird's wing, the arm part, is used for lift. The tip halves of the wings, the hand part, and especially the long flexible primary feathers, act as propellers and control surfaces. In this respect the design of a bird's wing differs radically from that of an aircraft, whose rotary propellers are not an integral part of the wing. In flapping flight each "propeller" moves in a semicircle—forward on the downward stroke, pulling the bird along, then backward (with negligible motive power) on the upbeat. At the moment of transition between downstroke and upstroke the flexible primary feathers become "slotted" to allow the air to slip through freely. Meanwhile the basal half of the wing continues to exert lift and to stabilize flight. The leading edge may be tilted upward, increasing the angle of attack as the wing meets the air stream, and thereby assuring greater lift.

Thousands of papers have been written on the aerodynamics of bird flight, but a bird's wing with its many flexible moving parts which twist and bend under the pressure of the air, particularly in flapping flight, defies the sort of critical analysis to which we can subject the rigid wing of an aircraft. Wind tunnels, smoke streams and mathematical formulas fail to give us more than an inkling of the answers. Perhaps electronic computers may someday help us define the forces acting on the wing of a bird in flight.

The smaller the bird the faster the wingbeat. A ruby-throated hummingbird may beat its wings at the fantastic rate of 50 to 70 times per second, which puts it within the wingbeat spectrum of sphinx moths and certain other large insects whose buzzy wing motion can be stopped photographically by using stroboscopic light. A mockingbird beats its wings 14 times per second, a pigeon 5 to 8, while a ponderous pelican may flap its huge wings as slowly as 1.3 times per second.

As the ornithologist Crawford Greenewalt has pointed out, when Nature designed the hummingbirds she changed her structural model. Whereas all other birds except swifts articulate their wings freely at the shoulder, elbow and wrist, the hummingbird articulates mainly at the shoulder. The elbow and wrist, though not "frozen," move less freely and the arm bones themselves are extremely short. The long paddle-like wing, which is virtually all hand, rotates at the shoulder very much like the wings of an insect. It may well be that size necessitated this change in wing design and it is perhaps no accident that hummingbirds bridge the gap between birds and insects. Imagine a hummingbird the size and weight of a swan: It has been computed that if its wings were built on the usual hummingbird model, they would be 32 feet (9.8 m) long!

Whereas most birds suggest conventional aircraft, hummingbirds operate more like helicopters, as ultra-high-speed pictures reveal. Crawford Greenewalt comments: "If a helicopter hovers, the rotor is in a plane parallel to the earth's surface—so are the wings of a hummingbird. As the helicopter moves forward or backward, the rotor tilts in the appropriate direction—so do the wings of a hummingbird. The helicopter can rise directly from a given spot without a runway for take-off—so can a hummingbird."

Hummingbirds are often credited with being the only birds able to fly backward. A downward scoop with the tail and a reversal of the wings which are literally mounted on a swivel allow the tiny bird to back away from a flower before making a fast getaway. Actually, as slow-motion movies show, certain other birds like the flycatchers and warblers can sometimes fly backward for a brief moment. Much the simplest form of flight, certainly much less

RUFFED GROUSE

GREAT BLUE HERON

RAVEN

OSTRICH

Four different kinds of walking feet are pictured here. The scaly fringes that appear every winter on the feet of the grouse (which does not migrate) help hold it up in snow, while the extra long toes and small webs of the marsh-wading heron keep it from sinking in the mud. The raven's all-purpose foot is suited for perching, walking or scratching. Drawn to scale below is the huge foot of the flightless ostrich. Like many grazing mammals, this grazing bird has only two toes.

complicated than flapping or hovering, is gliding flight. This, as we have seen, was undoubtedly the way the earliest birds flew, dawn creatures such as *Archaeopteryx* which are believed to have clambered up rocks and trees and launched themselves forth on set wings gliding as far as they were able or wanted to go. Swallows employ gliding flight—several strong wing strokes and a glide. So do pelicans traveling in formation, geese coming in for a landing, and many other birds. Gliding saves energy, but gravity and air conditions determine how far a bird can skim before it must flap again.

A much more specialized skill is soaring, which makes use of rising air currents so effectively that for long periods no flapping is required. The hawk watchers who converge by hundreds on Pennsylvania's Hawk Mountain on autumn weekends are often given a great exhibition of soaring flight at its best. If the wind is in the northwest and there is a strong updraft along the windward slope, the birds coast in a line along the ridge. An osprey clocked at two points along the ridge traveled 80 miles per hour (129 km/h) without flapping its wings. On warm sunny days when the thermals, those "winds that blow straight up," rise from the heated earth, the hawk watchers are treated to a magnificent display of true soaring—red-tailed hawks, turkey vultures and sometimes eagles swinging like sailplanes in wide and graceful circles on the invisible columns of rising air.

Soaring birds, with a large sail surface in proportion to their weight, fall into two very different types: (1) those with broad wings and fanlike tails as exemplified by many of the hawks, eagles and vultures, and (2) those with extremely long but relatively narrow wings, ocean wanderers such as gulls, frigate birds and albatrosses.

A VULTURE or a condor is a vision of effortless majesty as it glides on motionless wings along the face of a cliff, its primaries deeply slotted, like giant fingers, to counteract turbulence and to maintain stability in the uncertain air currents of the cordillera. No airplane would dare to negotiate the narrow canyons; no man-made craft is as maneuverable. Coming in for a landing the great bird first drops its "retractable landing gear"—its feet. Reducing its wing area with a mere shrug of the shoulders it loses altitude, then plunges straight at the ledge, so fast that a crash landing seems unavoidable. But at precisely the right moment it brings the braking action of its wings into play. The cupped wings act as flaps, the tail is lowered and spread, and the bird lands adroitly, its leg action absorbing the impact. For a brief moment it holds its wings high over its body, then neatly folds them in. This magical exhibition of purely physical control makes an airplane seem crude indeed.

The most effortless of all aerialists are the large albatrosses. Their realm is the sea where thermals are few and deflected air currents are ineffective for more than a meter or two above the waves. However, due to frictional drag, ocean winds are stronger at a height of 50 feet (15 m) than they are near the sea surface. The wandering albatross, with its wing span of 11 feet (3.4 m) or more, exploits this phenomenon in a methodical way. Once it has gained the level of the faster upper wind currents, it uses them to build speed in a long down-wind glide on scimitar-like wings. Then, almost brushing the wave crests, it turns into the slower surface winds, its great speed sending it zooming upward again. By thus alternating glide and zoom, the great bird can tack effortlessly over the sea for hours without beating its wings. The stronger the gale, the more it revels in its powers—the most efficient sailplane of them all.

A HUMMINGBIRD'S SKELETON AND THE HOLLOW THIGH BONE OF AN EXTINCT ELEPHANT BIRD SHOW HOW TINY AND HOW BIG BIRDS CAN BE

Built for a World of Air

Birds that fly—from the tiniest hummingbird to the largest albatross—are far more alike in their makeup than other groups of animals are. This is because flight has demanded that they have skeletons that are light but strong, muscles that are powerful but not a burden, feathers that conserve heat while providing lift and propulsion, and the sharpest eyes in the entire animal kingdom.

Flying Made Easier

The wing of a bird is constructed on sound aerodynamic principles. Not only is it streamlined to cut through the air with little drag, but it is also curved to produce lift, the force that keeps birds aloft. Air flowing past the leading edge and over the convex upper surface of the wing speeds up and tends to pull

LIFT is increased as the wing is tilted increasingly upward into the air stream. As long as the air flows smoothly, the wing flies (A). But if it is tilted sharply, turbulence sets in above the wing and lift is destroyed (B). On the leading edge of a bird's wing there is a group of feathers, the alula, which keeps the air flow smooth as the wing tilts (C) so that lift is maintained.

ALULA

FEATHERS FLATTENED FOR DOWNSTROKE

FEATHERS TWISTED FOR UPSTROKE

ON THE DOWNSTROKE, the power stroke in a bird's flight, the primary feathers hold firm, overlapping each other to present a closed surface to the air *(left)*. On the upstroke, however *(right)*, they open to allow air to slip through, making it easier to lift the wing. The alula, shown on the leading edge in the drawing at left, is under muscular control, ready when needed.

A (SHEARWATER)

B (PHEASANT)

C (ROUGH-LEGGED HAWK)

D (SWALLOW)

WING SHAPES reflect their uses. A long and narrow shape (A) is found among ocean gliders; a broad and slotted one (C) among land soarers. Type B provides power for quick escapes, D high speed on migrations.

42

away, thus creating a drop in pressure, while pressure on the concave undersurface remains fairly constant. It is the difference in the pressures above and below the wing that creates lift. As in airplanes, slots and flaps may increase or decrease lift. Wings vary among birds, reflecting the adaptations they have made to different niches in their environment. Gulls, dwelling in wide, open spaces, have evolved light, long, narrow wings for soaring on air currents. Pigeons, on the other hand, occupying a more cramped niche in which such currents are less dependable, have short, well-muscled wings which make them power fliers.

GLIDING ABILITY of birds varies widely. Here, greatly exaggerated vertically, are the distances achieved by four species. The hummingbirds, with tiny wings, can scarcely glide at all.

STATIC SOARING may occur when a broad-winged bird is carried aloft on warm air currents rising faster than the bird can fall. In still air, such a bird would glide from A to B position.

DYNAMIC SOARING permits an albatross to glide for hours over the ocean without flapping its wings. Here an albatross is shown rising against the wind from B level, where the wind is slowed by the friction of the waves, to A level, where it is blowing at a faster rate. Wheeling, the albatross glides downwind, gaining sufficient increased momentum to rise against it again.

A THERMAL, used by birds to soar, begins as a rising column of warm air (A), undercut by cold air (B). It continues up as a large warm air bubble (C and D), rising so strongly that a hawk circling in it rises too.

The Mechanics of Forward Flight

STRONG FLIERS like ducks do not swim through the air as many people believe; they are actually propeller-driven on the same basic principle as an airplane. In the case of a bird, however, the propellers are at the tips of the wings in the form of the primary feathers. The power is applied on the downstroke *(above, left)*. As the wing is pulled down against the resisting air, the tips of the primaries are bent upward and twisted at an angle to the wing as a whole. In this position they bite propeller-

The Mechanics of Hovering Flight

AERIAL ACROBATS, hummingbirds can fly straight up and even backward, but perhaps their most remarkable feat is hovering motionless in the air while sipping nectar from a flower. The secret of this ability lies in a wing structure quite different from that of most other birds. The wing as a whole is almost rigid with little movement at "wrist" and "elbow," and it is attached to the shoulder by a swivel joint. These views, from above and from the side, show how the whole wing acts like a helicopter's fashion into the air and as they are brought farther and farther down they are impelled forward, pulling the entire wing and hence the bird's body along with them. At the end of the downstroke the wing tips are on a level with the bill. On the upstroke, the primaries separate to permit easy passage of air; the wing tips move upward and backward against the air, still providing slight propulsion, while the inner part of each wing, close to the shoulder, provides lift. Then the cycle begins again.

rotor, but sculling back and forth instead of whirling around. On the forward stroke, the wing moves conventionally with the leading edge forward, angled slightly to provide lift but no thrust, as in the first six silhouettes. On the backstroke, the entire wing swivels almost 180 degrees at the shoulder (next six silhouettes); the leading edge is now turned backward so that on the backstroke the wing achieves the same effect of lift without propulsion. Thus the bird can hang motionless in the air.

45

AN OWL'S SKULL HAS THE CHARACTERISTIC AVIAN FEATURES OF LARGE EYE SOCKETS AND PAPER-THIN FUSED AND REINFORCED BONES

An Airy Frame

From the inside out, the skeletons of birds are natural marvels of flight engineering and structure. They combine lightness with strength, and in all their parts form beautifully follows function. In all birds that fly, the breastbone, though extremely thin and light, has a deep keel which not only makes it rigid, but, more importantly, provides a large surface for attachment of the powerful flight muscles. Many bones found in other higher vertebrates are missing in the birds, having been discarded in the evolutionary process of lightening the load; others normally jointed are fused for stress-resistance and lightness. Most bird bones are hollow and some are trussed inside to make them stronger while preserving their flexibility. The skeleton of a three- to four-pound (1.4- to 1.8-kg) frigate bird with a seven-foot (2.1-m) wingspread may weigh as little as four ounces (113 g)—less than the weight of the feathers.

DELICATE IN STRUCTURE, a gull's skeleton, here suspended from its wing, is strongest in the thorax, where reinforced ribs lock onto the breastbone. The spine is semifused for rigidity.

A HOLLOW WING BONE, the humerus of an eagle, is stiffened by struts. Air spaces in such bones are often continuations of air sacs in the birds' bodies and may even extend into their toes.

AN EGRET, a strong flier, takes off with its long, heavy neck outstretched. Once under way, it will retract the neck into an S and hold its legs stiffly out behind for balance. Because egrets have large wings, which are more efficient than smaller ones, they need flap them only about twice a second, in contrast to the 80 wingbeats per second of the tiniest hummingbirds.

A FULL-CHESTED, STUBBY-WINGED BOBWHITE QUAIL ZOOMS WITH A ROCKETING BURST FROM THE BRUSH WHERE IT WAS HIDING

A Powerful, Air-Cooled Engine

Birds flap their wings with powerful flight muscles which, to use automotive terms, come in two models: one designed to provide explosive bursts of speed for short distances, and another geared for endurance on long hauls. The bobwhite quail above, a ground bird like the chicken, has white flight muscles, quick to contract but meagerly supplied with blood vessels to carry oxygen and other fuel to the fibers and thus incapable of sustained action. For ground birds, flight is strictly a means of escape: If flushed several times, many species become exhausted and may even be picked up in the hand.

By contrast, strong fliers like the egret *(opposite)*, wild ducks, geese and other migrators have red flight muscles, plentifully supplied with blood vessels and not readily tired. Driving the wings, these muscles generate great heat and speed up the body's metabolism. Such heat would be killing were it not regulated by the respiratory system, the most efficient of any in the vertebrates. In addition to a pair of small, bright-red lungs, there are usually at least nine thin-walled air sacs with interconnecting chambers throughout the body. Not only do these bring supplies of oxygen to the tissues for burning, but also, perhaps through the evaporation of water, they help to keep the temperature to a tolerable limit.

AN ASIATIC FISHING OWL WINKS WITH A THIRD EYELID. FARSIGHTED OWLS HAVE POOR FOCUSING ABILITY AT CLOSE RANGE AND MUST BACK AWAY

VICTORIA CROWNED PIGEON

SATIN BOWERBIRD

SOUTHERN GROUND HORNBILL

LIKE WINDSHIELD WIPERS, nictitating membranes sweep across the eyeballs of a king vulture and a king penguin. Found in all birds, these transparent third eyelids clean and moisten the cornea. The king penguin can contract its pupil to a square.

Eyes That See Big—and Small

Though they look relatively small, hidden behind their lids and set like gems in protective rings of overlapping bone, birds' eyes are enormous. This is because flight demands that the image be big and all its details sharp. In many birds the eyes must also be able to register and react instantaneously to far objects and near ones—a swift out on patrol for food reacts with incredible speed to the flick of an insect crossing its path just a few centimeters ahead.

Birds' eyes vary in position and shape from species to species. Most birds have rather flat eyeballs with large retinas for images to play on, excellent for scanning the landscape. Birds of prey have rounder or almost tubular eyes. These take in less territory than flat ones do, but see farther and in greater detail, pinpointing living targets with the precision of a bombsight.

A bird has more sensory cells in its eyes than other animals have, particularly in the area of the fovea, a small depression in the retina at the point of acutest vision. The fovea's convex sides help magnify part of the image—as much as 30 per cent in some bird species. The retinas of hawks are from four to eight times as sensitive as those of humans, making these birds the keenest-sighted of all living things.

FROM NEAR OBJECTS TO SEE THEM WELL

PALLAS' SEA EAGLE   HOATZIN   DOUBLE-CRESTED CORMORANT

CONTOUR FEATHER

DOWN FEATHER

FILOPLUMES

OWL WING FEATHER

The Indispensable Feather

A bird's feathers have to do many things. Not only must they provide lift surfaces for wings and tail, but they must protect the bird against the weather and insulate it against loss of heat. Feathers come in almost infinite variety, but they fall into four main categories. Most numerous are the contour feathers which coat the body, giving it a streamlined shape. A house sparrow wears about 3,500 of these in winter, and they are so efficient at sealing in heat that it can easily maintain a normal temperature of 106.7° F. (41.5° C.) in below-freezing cold. Lying beneath them are the soft down feathers, also used for insulation. Scattered among both types are the hairlike filoplumes which sometimes protrude from the coat and may serve as a kind of decoration, or possibly as sensory organs. Flight feathers are the long stiff quills found on wings and tail. The webs are of unequal width, with the broader part forming the trailing edge. Among nocturnal owls, flight feathers are equipped with mufflers in the form of comblike projections and fringes for silent attacks on unwary prey.

FLIGHT FEATHER

THE SHIMMERING PLAY OF COLORS in a peacock's feather is caused by refraction and reflection of light from layers of horn that help to keep the true color, brown, from showing through.

A MOLTING TERN FLIES EASILY DESPITE MISSING FEATHERS, WHICH DROP OUT A FEW AT A TIME FROM EACH WING TO KEEP BALANCE

Keeping the Feathers in Shape

Tough though they are, the work that feathers do is tougher still, and to guard against their wearing or falling out prematurely, birds give them constant care. Most birds have oil glands at the bases of their tails, and preen themselves by smearing the oily secretion over their feathers with their beaks. Those which do not secrete oil preen with a powder made up of microscopic particles from feathers so delicate that they are constantly disintegrating into dust.

But even the best-kept feathers deteriorate, and most birds renew their coats at least once a year. Molting generally follows a regular pattern, ranging slowly and symmetrically over the bird, often progressing from rump to head. Ducks, geese and many other water birds shed most of their flight feathers at once and are thus temporarily grounded. At this time male ducks wear a dull coat called the "eclipse plumage." Occasionally all the feathers are shed simultaneously, as in penguins, whose old coat is pushed away by the emergence of new feathers growing from beneath. Because penguins are flightless, a complete molting is no hazard to them, but there are some birds which are made all but helpless by this. During a period of near-nakedness, the female African hornbill must stay in its walled-up nest cavity for safety and rely on the male for food.

FALL MOLTING of the rock ptarmigan helps to camouflage this ground bird of the tundra and alpine slopes by giving it a patchwork appearance. Brown feathers are replaced by white ones.

WINTER PLUMAGE of the ptarmigan is pure white to blend with snow. The spring molting, triggered perhaps by the change in temperature, will produce an almost all-brown summer coat.

TWISTING ITS NECK INTO AN EIGHT, A FLAMINGO GOES ABOUT THE TASK OF ARRANGING AND OILING ITS FEATHERS

UPSIDE-DOWN HEAD of a short-eared owl shows the extraordinary flexibility which allows these birds to swivel their heads in almost every direction. This one is trying to focus on a close-up object—the camera.

3

Birds as Food Gatherers

NEARLY every category of animal and plant life on earth is exploited by some bird. Even the remains of whales and elephants find their way into the diets of scavenging gulls and vultures (and so, occasionally, does man himself). At the other end of the avian food spectrum is one of the most minute of primitive plants, blue-green alga, the main source of subsistence for the 3,000,000 or more lesser flamingos that crowd the salt lakes of East Africa. In fact, one of the reasons that flamingos, birds of ancient lineage, still exist at all is because they can use this environment that few other creatures can exploit.

The varied hosts of birds that live on earth today survive because they have been able to carve out special niches of their own, either geographically or environmentally. Although unrelated birds with somewhat different habits may overlap in their territories, evolution seldom permits closely related species—two kinds of jays, for example—to occupy the same territory and exploit the identical niche in the same way.

Every environment except for the truly sterile areas of the world has its specific birds. They have developed along with the food resources in the various living places—the forests, mountains, grasslands, scrub, marshes, deserts, tundra, rivers, lakes, islands and the sea, and lately the cities and farms. The association is not accidental, but is the result of natural selection over long periods of time toward a more successful life.

It has often been claimed that were it not for the birds, insects would inherit the earth. This is clearly an exaggeration, for insects have effective predators and parasites within their own ranks (birds, incidentally, do not discriminate between "pest" insects and "beneficial" insects). But birds do exert great controlling pressures at the critical periods. Warblers and other migrants arrive at precisely the time when myriads of small insect larvae are hatching on emerging leaves. They continue the assault in the succeeding weeks when their hungry young, which may consume nearly their own weight in food daily, make constant demands. A pair of magnolia warblers nesting in a spruce forest in Maine will feed their large young a beakful of insects on an average of once every four minutes. Adult birds, on the other hand, require less fuel. The high water content of caterpillars and other insects may result in an adult insectivorous bird eating 40 per cent of its weight daily, but a seedeater may eat only 10 per cent.

The insects, which have invaded nearly every terrestrial environment on earth, are unable to evade the birds that probe the soil, turn over the leaf litter, search the bark, dig into the trunks of trees, scrutinize every twig and living leaf. The water is no safe refuge, nor is the air, nor the dark of night. There is a bird of some sort to hunt nearly every insect. Warblers and vireos methodically work the leaves while swallows, swifts and other hunters of flying-insect prey spend most of their waking hours on the wing, ranging hundreds of miles daily in their aerial forays.

In tropical America a number of soberly colored ant birds specialize in following the large swarms of army ants, feeding on the many other insects that are flushed up as the army advances over the jungle floor. Similarly, in Africa, many insect-hunting birds take advantage of the grass fires set by native tribesmen to improve the pasturage. Ground hornbills stalk close to the smouldering tussocks while kestrels hover in the smoke and rollers perch nearby. Grazing animals also act as insect-flushing agents, and in East Africa the bustards, cattle egrets, bee-eaters and other species live in intimate association with zebras, antelope and other herd animals.

M ANY birds in their search for insects are preoccupied with the trunks of trees. These include the nuthatches, treecreepers, woodcreepers and even some wood warblers; but none are as well designed for the job as the woodpeckers. These specialized hammerers spend most of their lives in a perpendicular stance, clamped against a trunk or a branch, the stiff tail acting as a brace and the deeply curved claws, two forward, two aft on each foot, clutching the rough bark. The straight beak, hard as a chisel, is driven in triphammer blows by powerful muscles in the head and neck while other muscles help the thick skull absorb the shock. When a borer is uncovered, an extremely long, barbed tongue snakes in to hook it. The woodpeckers, an old family numbering more than 200 living members, probably developed their skill as far back as the Eocene, more than 50 million years ago.

One of the famous Darwin finches of the Galápagos, the woodpecker finch, has ingeniously circumvented the woodpecker's labors to get at wood-boring grubs that it cannot reach with its bill. Picking up a slender twig or a cactus-needle two inches (5 cm) long or so, it deftly pokes it into the hole, much as one would spear a cocktail snack with a toothpick, and out comes the grub. This is one of only a few birds that actually make use of a tool to get their food.

In the beginning, all birds probably ate animal food. Seed-eating is almost certainly a later specialization. A suggestive clue is the fact that nearly all seed-eating birds start off their newly hatched young on insects, then gradually make the switch to a vegetable diet. Pigeons, an exception, get around this by feeding their young on a secretion called "pigeon's milk."

The great proliferation of seed-eating birds must have taken place fairly recently in evolutionary history, mostly in the last 10 million years, after the Miocene, when the seed-bearing plants, especially the grasses and sedges, had their great spread. Birds of several orders eat seeds, but it is among the various families of perching birds, the Passeriformes, that we most often find the stout conical bill that is adapted for seed-cracking. It is particularly typical of the finches and the buntings, which many evolutionists consider among the most recently developed families of birds. However, some taxonomists cannot agree as to where some of the finchlike birds should be placed or how many family stocks should be recognized. As we have seen, such highly functional food-getting structures as bills may not always indicate blood ties, but perhaps merely convergence or parallelism of anatomical development—i.e., the habit of seed-cracking has evolved, through natural selection, a bill that is capable of cracking seeds.

Roots, tubers, grass, leaves, buds, seeds, fruit pulp, nectar, pollen and sap of various plants find their way into the diet of birds. On the other hand very few birds eat fungi, lichens and some of the other more primitive plants.

To those of us who live in the temperate parts of the Northern Hemisphere it comes as a surprise to learn that nearly one fifth of all the world's birds feed mainly on nectar. A bird watcher in New England is aware that ruby-throated hummingbirds live on nectar and that northern orioles sometimes poke at blossoms and appear to be getting nectar from them, but he finds it difficult to believe that more than 1,600 other species of birds on five continents take part in nectar feeding.

Most of these birds, to be sure, are in the Southern Hemisphere. The hummingbirds, a rainbow-hued galaxy of about 300 species, are the most efficient of all the nectar gatherers by far, hovering before flowers and probing them deftly with needle-like bills. The tiniest hummingbird, the bee hummingbird of Cuba, is only two and one fourth inches (5.7 cm) long, smaller than some of the sphinx moths that these minuscule birds so closely resemble in their contour, wing length and wing action.

Small though it is, the amount of energy burned up by a hummer is phenomenal, as the ruby-throated hummingbird shows. If a normal 170-pound (77-kg) man expended energy at the rate of this little bird, he would have to eat, in a single day, 285 pounds (129 kg) of hamburger or double his own weight in potatoes. Crawford Greenewalt cites an even more astonishing statistic: A man expending energy at the rate of a hovering hummingbird would have to evaporate about 100 pounds (45 kg) of perspiration per hour to keep his skin temperature below the boiling point of water!

In spite of their strong powers of flight, the hummingbirds have never bridged the gap between the New World and the Old. However, a large family of Old World birds, the sunbirds (Nectariniidae), numbering more than 100 species, attempts to fill the flower niche. Most sunbirds are not much larger than the general run of hummingbirds and many are as gaudily colored. But they cannot

AFTER A WOODPECKER PECKS

For a woodpecker, chiseling into trees with its bill is only the first step in getting the grubs that live there. It then uses a flexible tongue for penetrating deep into the galleries that wood borers make in trees and snaking out its food. This raises the question: Where does the woodpecker store such a tongue in its small head? Actually, the tongue is rather short. It is part of an apparatus of bones and elastic tissue (shown in color) that goes under the jaw, up around the back of the head and anchors itself in the right nostril, leaving the left one free for breathing (bottom drawing). When this apparatus, known as the hyoid, is slid around the head, the tongue is protruded (upper drawings).

A BILL FOR ANY DIET

COCKATOO

The hooked beak of this seedeater is a powerful and efficient nutcracker. After the nut or seed is cracked, the bird picks out the meat with a strong, supple tongue.

CROSSBILL

This scissors-like bill is designed to lever the seeds out of evergreen cones. Other birds must either wait until the cones dry out, or laboriously pick them apart.

OYSTERCATCHER

This bird's bill is higher than it is broad and is inserted like a chisel in partly open oyster shells, paralyzing the occupants before they are able to snap shut.

compare with hummingbirds in their flying skill; they must perch while they sip and only rarely do they hover before a blossom.

Nectar feeders must be flexible to prosper, able to follow the blossoming of the flowers. Hawaiian honey creepers travel in loose flocks from one section of forest on the volcanic slopes to another, their movements dictated by the blooming of the ohia, mamane and other native trees. Hummingbirds in the western United States migrate through the Pacific lowlands when the early spring flowers are at their best, but go up to the high alpine meadows in late summer when the valleys lie parched and brown.

A large branch of the parrot clan, the lorikeets of the Australasian region, specializes in nectar feeding in a crude fashion, crushing the bristly blossoms of eucalypti and other flowering trees and sopping up the sticky juices with their fringe-tipped tongues. Like other parrots, the lorikeets enjoy company and travel the mountain forests in large gangs, concentrating where the blossoms are thickest and signaling noisily to other passing flocks to join them. Twittering and chattering, they pause briefly to decorate a tree with their brilliant colors, then rush away toward new horizons. On Australia's Queensland coast, a beekeeper, Alex Griffiths, has attracted hundreds of rainbow lorikeets with pans of honey to his home in the town of Currumbin. They have accepted his friendship completely, freely perching on his hands, his shoulders and his head. Now the place is a sanctuary and as many as 500 lorikeets come each afternoon to feed on honey and to delight the crowds of human observers who sometimes outnumber the birds.

Tropical fruit-eating birds, like the nectar feeders, are usually gaudily colored and most of them are noisy. Parrots fly in flocks or in twosomes over the tropical forests shrieking loudly. A feeding flock hidden in the foliage below shrieks back, inviting them to share in their good fortune. It is to their mutual advantage that they are gaudy and noisy for in the dark jungle a tree laden with ripening fruit may be far from the next one.

In marked contrast to them are the soft-voiced waxwings, sleek, crested birds dressed in muted browns and grays. Cedar waxwings may winter as far north as southern Canada but they also go as far south as Panama, traveling in tight flocks and lingering only when they find a treeful of berries. The bird watcher cannot predict their arrivals and departures, for they stay in a neighborhood only as long as the fruit lasts. Thus the well-named Bohemian waxwing will be found in Scandinavia as long as the rowan tree has fruit, but when the berries give out it may cross the North Sea to invade England.

Five sevenths of the surface of the globe is sea. For every square mile (2.6 km²) of land there are two and a half square miles (6.5 km²) of salt water, yet birds that we might properly call sea birds aggregate only about three per cent of the world's species—roughly 260, made up of a dozen families. Some, like most of the gulls and terns, the cormorants, frigate birds and pelicans, stick rather closely to the coasts, so that the truly pelagic birds number less than 150 species.

The sea is rich in life and those birds that have adapted to its quixotic winds and waves and have accepted its harsh terms find a bountiful larder. The oceans are not one uniform ecological block. Planktonic life, the pasturage of the sea, made up of countless minute, floating marine organisms, is not distributed evenly like sugar stirred into a cup of tea; it runs in streaks or ribbons, concentrated by the sea currents and upwellings. Where the organisms are thick the birds assemble. The colder ocean currents have a far higher density of plankton than warmer areas. This directly affects bird life. Watching from the ship rail in tropical oceans one sees but a tiny fraction of the birds that he would see during the same amount of time in northern or far southern waters.

The cold Humboldt Current, for example, flowing northward off the west coast of South America, brings riches to Peru in the form of millions of guanay cormorants, gannet-like piqueros and pelicans which deposit their nitrate-rich guano on the offshore islets. The food cycle of the sea is to be seen here in its most dynamic form. The prevailing southerly winds force the surface water away from the rainless desert coast, allowing colder water to rise from the bottom to take its place. As this water wells upward it brings with it nitrogenous and phosphorous compounds released by the decay of myriads of marine animals and plants. Microscopic algae, tinging the water green, use these nutrients and they in turn are the food base for astronomical numbers of anchovies. Little fish attract bigger fish and birds. No other coastal waters on earth support more sea birds. One oceanographer, Dr. Gerald Posner, once estimated that "the yearly consumption of fish by guano birds about equals the total annual commercial fisheries catch for the entire United States."

ANHINGA

Also called darters or snakebirds, anhingas impale fish under the water on their spearlike beaks. Long sinuous necks and webbed feet help them in their fishing.

In the Western Hemisphere, only the Pribilofs in the Bering Sea can match the numbers of sea birds found off the coast of Peru. Here two very similar members of the auk family, the common murre and the thick-billed murre, live side by side on the sea cliffs, along with two species of puffins and two of kittiwake gulls. Biologists wonder: Where is the competition between species here? The two murres seem equally abundant and so do the two puffins. Perhaps each has a different food pattern of which we are not yet aware. As for the two gulls, the red-legged kittiwake is much the scarcer, perhaps a relict species losing out to the more successful black-legged kittiwake.

Although there are roughly 260 birds that we classify as sea birds, there are fully 600 others that we might call water birds—birds of the lakes, shores, estuaries, swamps and marshes. Some of these, like the scoters, eiders, grebes and loons, may even become sea birds for part of the year, or at least birds of the coastal waters.

Loons are among the very few birds with solid, heavy bones. Lack of buoyancy is an asset to a bird that spends most of its time in submarine pursuit of fish. And loons dive far and deep—one was recovered from a fisherman's net 240 feet (73 m) down. Loons and grebes are both ill-fitted for locomotion on land, so much so that they may avoid taking their feet out of the water (except to fly) for months on end; but they will finally do so only when it is necessary to clamber onto their nests.

The long-legged "glamor birds," the herons, storks, ibises, spoonbills and cranes, numbering about 120 species, are marshland associates that stalk fish, frogs, small reptiles, crustaceans and large insects. Their stiltlike legs are counterbalanced with equally long necks which make useful periscopes above the marsh grass. Followers of Izaak Walton have often noticed that some of the best fishing is downstream from a heronry. The nitrogenous droppings of the birds enrich the water, fish multiply and the herons exact tribute in return, pointing the way for anglers.

The smaller waders, the snipe, sandpipers, plovers and their relatives, denied access to deeper water, concentrate along the shoreline where they catch sand fleas, probe for marine worms, eat mosquito larvae, take small crabs, or knock limpets off rocks. If it is edible, there is a wader to eat it. Ducks of a feather

FLAMINGO

Flamingos live on the organic matter found in mud. Their bent bills, fringed at the edges, filter out mud and water and retain the minute plants and animals.

A KESTREL'S DIET

Because of their high metabolic rate, birds have enormous appetites in proportion to their size and weight: The smaller and lighter the bird, the more prodigious is its food intake. The three piles shown here represent a year's food of an American kestrel, which breeds and winters in Michigan. The smallest pile, 5 per cent, is insects; the next, 15 per cent, is small birds; the largest, 80 per cent, is rodents. It is estimated that a kestrel may eat as many as 290 mice in one year.

flock together and although a dozen kinds might consort on a lake or a bay each species has its traditional stopping places. In winter, canvasbacks favor the bay near New York's La Guardia Airport, or the Chesapeake below Baltimore where wild celery grows. Wigeon are grazers and swarm over the golf courses of some West Coast cities, while shovelers sift the mud in adjacent ponds. Brant resort to the eelgrass beds of certain salt bays while rafts of scoters dive for mussels in the rougher water off nearby coastal headlands. The mergansers are fish ducks, and a thousand rivers and bays know their underwater activity. Although the 150 or so species of ducks, geese and swans superficially resemble one another and some may compete, few if any share precisely the same requirements. Each is able to exploit its own special niche in the water world a little more efficiently than the others.

We are reminded all the time that both the birds and their environments evolved together. A hunter who brings down a duck sometimes notices tiny oval leaflets adhering to the feathers. This is duckweed, *Lemna*, which produces few seeds; its principal way of reproducing is to bud. A lobe appears on the small green leaflet which grows and then separates as a daughter plant, capable of reproducing on its own. All marsh ducks eat *Lemna*, which often sticks to them as they swim through masses of it and is thus carried to new ponds and puddles, insuring survival for both ducks and duckweed.

Birds of prey, more than 400 species, divide nature into two parts: day and night. Two thirds of their number—the hawks, eagles, falcons and vultures—are diurnal, going about their business between sunrise and sunset. The other third, the owls, are mainly night hunters. In North America the great horned owl emerges at dusk to prowl over the same terrain where the red-tailed hawk soared at noon. Similarly, the barred owl dominates the swampy woodlands while the red-shouldered hawk sleeps. Nocturnal habits, therefore, are no insurance for the safety of small mammals, every one of which is a potential meal for some predator. The huge binocular eyes of owls have great light-gathering power and their ears, long asymmetrical slits hidden behind the facial disks, can pinpoint the rustling of a mouse in the darkest wood. L. R. Dice, experimenting with long-eared and barn owls, found that they could locate a dead mouse in light ten to one hundred times dimmer than that needed by the human eye, and could capture a live mouse in total darkness.

The method of killing used by a hawk or an owl is to plunge at its prey and to strike or clutch with hooked talons. Vultures usually (but not always) eschew living prey and therefore have no need for the strongly curved "meat hooks" of their diurnal relatives; their feet are relatively weak.

No bird in the world is better equipped for pursuit than the peregrine falcon, bulletheaded, broad in the shoulder and tapering to the tail, a powerful, perfectly streamlined machine whose pointed wings can put it into a power dive estimated to reach 175 miles per hour (282 km/h). But the peregrine is effective only in open terrain; for this reason falconry as a sport has never caught on in wooded eastern North America as it has on the moorlands of north England and Scotland. Most falcons are strong fliers of the open country, although some of the smaller ones, the kestrels, are more like helicopters, hovering for mice, grasshoppers and other petty prey.

The bird hawks, the Accipiters, on the other hand, are adapted for the surprise attack. They have evolved a short rounded wing, which seems perfectly designed for dodging through trees and for quick maneuvering. The big goshawk specializes in grouse and small mammals, while the little sharp-shin takes warblers. For every successful try at a bird there are a number of misses. The bird caught, more often than not, is the marginal individual, sick, old or unwary. European sparrow hawks and their American equivalent, the sharp-shin, have become very rare during recent decades, because they have been feeding mainly on songbirds stricken with toxic pesticides, and thus many were fatally stricken themselves.

Contrary to the views held by many sportsmen, the birds of prey are not creatures of pure destruction. Because their victims for the most part are the weak and the unfit, they tone up the vitality of their prey through natural selection—they are necessary to the health of the wildlife community. In the early '50s when the rabbit plague myxomatosis was deliberately introduced into France nearly all the rabbits of western Europe succumbed in blind agony. Mortalities ran between 95 and 99 per cent, but in the Marismas of southern Spain the disease never reached epidemic proportions. There the population of kites, eagles and other birds of prey, more numerous than elsewhere in Europe, caught the infected rabbits so quickly that the disease never succeeded in getting out of hand.

Though large birds of prey like eagles may be forced to live in solitary splendor so that they can maintain a dependable prey population, sociability has its rewards for some species. Vultures are dependent on the accident of death, whether caused by disease, starvation, fire or by that archpredator, man. A windfall often means food for all. Every big-game hunter who has gone on safari in Africa knows how quickly vultures seem to communicate knowledge of a kill. The first soaring birds to spot carrion seem to betray it to more distant birds by their maneuvers. Within the space of minutes a great wheel of birds zeros in on the target while new recruits arrive from all points of the compass. A century ago a hunter who had been killing antelope recorded that no fewer than 150 California condors were attracted to the scene. (There are probably only about 40 of these big birds alive today.)

BLACK vultures were once accused of spreading hog cholera, but actually no more efficient sanitary squad exists than these or, for that matter, vultures in general. Their digestive system destroys bacteria and even their excretions probably are an effective antiseptic, for instead of squirting clear as an eagle does they whitewash their own legs. The head, which comes into contact with putrid flesh, is naked, exposing infectious bacteria to the purifying rays of the sun. The marabou, an African stork with the habits of a vulture, also has a bare head and defecates on its own feet.

The diurnal birds of prey, from six-inch-long (15-cm) falconets of Asia to the great monkey-eating eagle of the Philippines, have exploited nearly every source of vertebrate prey smaller than themselves. The secretary bird, so-called because it has a score of penlike quills dangling from behind its ears, specializes in snakes and its long legs are protected with heavy plating. The honey buzzard, fond of wasps, actually has protective facial armor, small hard scalelike feathers between the eye and the bill and forehead. The Everglade kite, which feeds only on *Pomacea* snails, carries an exaggerated hook on its upper mandible. For many years ornithologists thought this was for scooping out the snail, but apparently it is not. Instead, the bird patiently holds the mollusk in its talons until it cautiously ventures from its shell; then, with a precise prick, the hook pierces the nerve center and the paralyzed snail is consumed. Every now and then a bird seems to hit on a special way of making a living. Eons ago a vulture, somewhere in Africa, must have idly pecked at the fruit of an oil palm and, finding it edible, made a habit of feeding on it. Today the palm-nut vulture eats little else except for an occasional dead fish.

In northern South America another aberrant bird specializes in the oily fruits of palms—the unbelievable oilbird, or guacharo. Related to the whippoorwills and other nightjars and the only vegetarian among a strictly insectivorous order of birds, it plucks the fruit while hovering like a helicopter. It is said to travel at night as much as 50 miles (80 km) to find ripe fruit, returning by dawn like one of the tortured demons or lost souls of Bald Mountain to hide in caves so deep and dark that it must use a sort of sonar to find its way about. Bats have in their ears a similar device, with which they measure the distance of objects by emitting supersonic squeaks. The oilbird's clicks, however, are audible to human ears, with a frequency of 7,000 cycles per second.

Another group of specialists, the honey guides, give us pause to ponder the intricacies of evolution. Dull-colored and as unprepossessing as sparrows, the greatest claim to oddity of this mainly African family is its addiction to beeswax. One species, the greater honey guide, attracts the attention of a honey badger or a baboon, or even a primitive African tribesman, by chattering and, making sure it is followed, guides the chosen animal or human to the bees' nest. Waiting patiently while its partner has a go at the honey, it finally helps itself to the bits of honeycomb lying about. Normally beeswax is indigestible, but Herbert Friedmann proved that the bacterial flora within the bird's intestines turn it into useful food.

Some birds are not averse to poaching and piracy. The bald eagle often highjacks the osprey returning to its eyrie with a fish. The eagle, faster and more powerful, harries the osprey until it drops its catch and, plunging quickly, snatches the fish before it hits the water. Frigate birds harass boobies when they return from their fishing at sea, forcing them to disgorge. Similarly, one whole family of birds, the jaegers and skuas, gull-like sea birds of piratical habits, make their living partly by raiding gulls and terns.

The wigeon, a dabbling duck, cannot dive easily as does the canvasback. It overcomes this handicap by waiting until the canvasback surfaces with a mouthful of wild celery, then rushes in to snatch it away. Laughing gulls use a similar technique when a brown pelican surfaces with a pouchful of small fish: During the brief moment when the pelican allows the water to drain from its open pouch the gulls snatch their share.

In contrast to the specialists, some birds are true omnivores and will eat almost anything. Crows and jays, always resourceful, will eat young birds in season, as well as baby mice, insects, grain, fruits or carrion. But even they have their preferences and these may change seasonally.

The question is, what is a balanced diet for a bird? The birds are obviously opportunists, taking whatever is in most plentiful supply within the limits of their various basic needs. Availability is a key factor in all predation, whether it involves the goshawk that takes a pheasant instead of a grouse, or the American robin that eats a tomato worm instead of a cecropia larva. Probably no bird has ever eliminated its food supply; were it to do so it would eliminate itself. Usually when one item of food becomes scarcer the bird turns to something else within its food spectrum. It crops the expendable surpluses, seldom digging deep into capital. And through the wisdom of natural selection the future takes care of itself.

A NORTHERN SHRIKE STORES ITS FOOD BY IMPALING IT ON TWIGS OR THORNS. HERE THE VICTIMS ARE A GRASSHOPPER AND A SMALL FROG

Food from Every Habitat

One reason birds are so abundant is that they can eat almost anything, not only plants, insects and even mammals of some size but also food that is inaccessible to other creatures. Many are omnivorous and show little specialization. Others, however, which have concentrated on a particular food source, have evolved unique equipment and strange ways for getting—and even storing—a meal.

FLIPPED ON ITS BACK, a brown pelican makes an awkward entry. Although expert divers, they can be upset by sudden gusts or updrafts.

The Master Divers

Some special problems confront air-breathing birds that enter the water to feed on fish and other marine creatures. Whether they plunge from the sky or dive from the surface, they must be able to come up quickly before their air runs out and seize and hold their prey without gulping too much water.

Pelicans, gannets and boobies are among the birds that have solved the resurfacing problem by evolving inflatable air sacs under the skin. These not only make them more buoyant, but also absorb much of the shock of impact. The loon, a surface diver, has learned simply to hold its breath. Although it usually surfaces in less than a minute, it is known to stay under water for as long as five minutes while swimming for hundreds of meters. The osprey, like any hawk, avoids both of these problems by grabbing its victim from the water with razor-sharp talons.

A DIVE-BOMBING ATTACK by brown pelicans begins when the pair peels off, extending their necks and pointing their beaks like spears *(left)*.

ON TARGET, a pelican's dive ends successfully *(right)*. The fish will end up in the pouch along with liters of water which must be drained.

A GREAT SPOTTED WOODPECKER, faced with the problem of getting a round, rolling hazelnut to stay still long enough to be opened, solves it by ramming the nut into a makeshift vise it has chiseled out of the tree bark, then splits it with a few raps of its beak. For catching insects, this European bird has another weapon—a tongue with tiny barbs at the tip for spearing its prey.

Drills, Hammers, Spoons and Spears

Food that is hard to get at—the kernel in a nut, the grub under the bark of a tree—is the particular specialty of some orders of birds which have evolved highly developed tools designed to perform one job well. Beaks are the primary instruments, and in jays, parrots, nutcrackers and woodpeckers they are as hard as flint, built to gouge, crack, hammer and drill. The common grackle, going still further, has a kind of built-in lathe, a tough ridge in its palate which, as it rotates an acorn in its mouth, literally saws it open. Many woodpeckers, in addition, have long sticky tongues for snapping up insects. The green woodpecker, for example, can send its prying tongue deep into ant tunnels to lap up food *(below)*.

A GREEN WOODPECKER extends its long and sinuous tongue some four inches (10 cm) into the galleries of an ant nest, here cut away and walled off with a pane of glass. The tongue is coated with saliva and flexible enough to follow every curve of the gallery, picking up adults and pupae alike which the bird skillfully works backward toward its bill until it has a mouthful.

A GREEN BARBET of India, its mouth full of berries, drops from its perch an instant before spreading its wings. Although related to the woodpecker, the barbet has a less specialized beak. Instead of chiseling hardwood, it plucks berries or digs for grubs in soft ground or rotted trees. It is a wasteful feeder, harvesting more than it consumes, but does not store its food.

The Master Hunters

In a sense, any bird that feeds on another living creature, even an insect, is a predator. But the true birds of prey are those specially equipped to take on larger animals, from mice and rabbits to snakes and small deer—the hawks and eagles which hunt by day, and the owls which take over at night. Ranging

RUFFLED AND BADLY WINDED, BUT TRIUMPHANT, THE OWL HAS MANAG

FALLING SILENTLY, a great horned owl aims for the head of an eastern coachwhip snake. Although owls have excellent night vision, they rely on extraordinarily acute hearing for attacks.

MISJUDGING ITS STRIKE, the owl hits too far back of the snake's head to immobilize it and is knocked flat by its flailing tail. The frantic snake tries to get away but the owl hangs on.

A FURIOUS BATTLE ensues as the owl tries to kill the snake before the latter can coil around the owl's body in an attempt to suffocate it. Such fights can end in death for both combatants.

in size from the tiny falconet of Asia to the great, monkey-eating eagles of the Philippines, the predators rely on sharp-clawed feet for killing and beaks for chopping and ripping. Feet vary according to use. Thus African hawk eagles have long toes for catching birds on the wing, while owls have short, powerful feet for clutching small mammals and reptiles. All birds of prey have compact, hooked beaks, and the falcon's is also notched for snapping the neck vertebrae of its victims. Sometimes, as in the case of the owl seen here, a first strike fails and a real fight follows.

TO KEEP ITS GRIP ON THE SNAKE'S BODY WITH BOTH TALONS AND FINISHES IT OFF WITH A LETHAL BITE JUST BACK OF THE VULNERABLE HEAD

SIGHTING A POSSUM, a young red-tailed hawk hunches forward ready to plunge. Red-tails perch for hours at a time on a favorite roost, searching for movements that could mean a meal.

An Apprentice Predator

The business of hunting, while motivated by instinct, is also a craft. Young birds learn it only after long practice, and experience teaches them what they can safely handle in the way of prey. Most immature birds attack whatever tempts them on a hit-or-miss basis until they have had some possibly painful lessons; what they will get will be the very small, the very young and the very old.

The red-tailed hawk here is an immature bird whose judgment may have been further impaired by

SURPRISED BY THE POSSUM'S SHARP TEETH AND WILLINGNESS TO FIGHT BACK, THE YOUNG RED-TAIL NERVOUSLY FLAPS ITS WINGS AND LURCHES several weeks spent in captivity. Nevertheless, it belongs to a species that does kill possums, and when this one saw a possum, instinct launched it to the attack. But where an experienced adult bird would have struck fast and hard, the youngster, not quite sure of itself, failed to press its dive all the way home. As a result, instead of having a dead or stunned animal in its talons, it found itself facing one that was very much alive. Thus threatened, it abandoned the attack completely and hurriedly backed away.

CHECKING ITS DIVE too soon, the hawk spreads its wings, apparently sensing the possum may be a bit too big for it. This gives the possum time to scramble around and face its attacker.

BACKWARD. HAND-REARED, THIS BIRD PAID NO ATTENTION TO THE CAMERA BUT BEHAVED AS A WILD HAWK WOULD HAVE IN A SIMILAR SITUATION

The Profits of Fraternization

Like many animals, birds occasionally find their food in association with other creatures, frequently to the benefit of both. The partnership may be one-sided, as in the case of a sparrow picking up seeds from the droppings of other animals, or the ptarmigan, which eats insects dug up by caribou. But sometimes the arrangement is mutually beneficial, as in the cleaning arrangement in which the African tick bird removes vermin from large mammals.

In an extreme example, the honey guide, a small forest bird, will lure a badger to a wild bees' nest by chattering, flying ahead a meter or two and chattering again. The badger will find the nest, eat the honey and leave the comb and grubs for the bird. But the red-billed oxpecker *(bottom right)* plays a dual role: It not only acts as doctor to the rhinoceros, picking ticks from its hide, but also warns its host of danger with its agitated chatter.

A GRAZING OSTRICH rooting about in search of grass, seeds and insects works over the same African plains territory as a gazelle and a wart hog. Each animal may involuntarily lead the others to a source of food and even alert them to danger.

FLITTING CATTLE EGRETS skip under foot or perch on the backs of African Ankole cattle. Though they feed primarily on the insects stirred up as the cattle graze, they have also found a source of food in the flies on the backs of the cattle themselves.

SCAVENGING GULLS wait for a pair of big Alaskan brown bears to finish their meal of salmon. When the bears depart, the gulls devour whatever is left, an arrangement apparently satisfactory to both parties.

A NIBBLING OXPECKER pulling parasites from a rhinoceros wound secures a meal and helps keep the large animal free of infection. The crowned lapwing in the foreground feeds on insects the rhino turns up.

RUFOUS HORNBILL

ARIEL TOUCAN

PARAKEET

SHOEBILL

KING VULTURE

CARACARA

Beaks Both Useful and Bizarre

The oddly shaped beaks on these pages all have one thing in common: They perform specific functions. Most were shaped by eating habits, though some hornbill species use their great and gaudy bills as a defense against marauding monkeys and snakes, while the toucan's lobster-claw beak serves as a mark of recognition and may figure in courtship display. The carrion-eating king vulture and the caracara have sharp hooks at the tips of their beaks for tearing hides and meat. The shoebill's beak also ends in a hook, but it is flat and serrated as an aid in holding slippery frogs. The parakeet's strong, curved bill is well adapted for cracking seeds, gouging out chunks of fruit and even for climbing. The protruding lower half of the black skimmer's trowel-like beak is useful for scooping up fish out of water.

A BLACK SKIMMER PICKS UP SMALL FISH ON THE WING BY PLOWING THE WATER WITH ITS LOWER BIL

CANADA GEESE float on a pond in North Carolina after an October flight from their Hudson Bay nesting grounds. With food available at this private refuge, they will remain until the first full moon in March.

4

How Many Birds?

Any attempt to reduce to manageable proportions a concept as enormous and wide-ranging as the world's population of birds must begin by fitting them into some system of categories. An obvious way to do this is to consider them in terms of their distribution and for more than a century naturalists have been trying out various ways of doing just that. P. L. Sclater was the first to look at the bird population from a worldwide point of view, in 1857, when he suggested a system organized on basic geographical areas, believing like so many other men of his time that every species of animal must have been created within and over the geographic area it occupied.

Sclater's system divided the world into six major regions: the Nearctic, comprising North America north of central Mexico; the Neotropical, including Central and South America; the Palearctic, which took in Europe, the northwest corner of Africa and Asia without the subcontinent of India and the southeastern peninsular countries; the Ethiopian, including most of Africa and also southern Arabia; the Oriental, comprising tropical India, Burma, Malaysia and the southeast; and the Australian, made up of Australia, New Zealand and the adjacent islands. On a map of the world, this division would appear as six great geographic regions, overlapping here and there as to continents but nonetheless quite clearly delimited and defined. Darwin's theories in the *Origin of Species*, published soon after, knocked the props from under Sclater's basic reasoning about the geographic origin of animals, but his concept of zoogeographical regions, for reasons of practicality is still accepted with some modifications by naturalists today. For example, because of the massive intermingling of New World and Old World birds in the more northern areas where they have crossed the Bering Strait between Asia and America, many biologists prefer to lump the Nearctic and Palearctic into one major region called the Holarctic.

A NORTH AMERICAN concept was worked out some 35 years after Sclater's worldwide system by Clinton Hart Merriam after climbing one of the San Francisco Peaks in Arizona. Starting in the desert, Merriam noted that as he ascended higher and higher the bird life of the areas he passed through changed. As he left the desert area many species dropped behind, to be replaced by others among the piñon pines and still others as he reached the higher fir forests. The birds and other animals were obviously associated with the plant life, and climbing the mountain was like traveling northward, with altitude compensating for latitude. Though other naturalists had noticed this before him, Merriam was the first to see it as a practical demonstration of a method by which the distribution of North American plants and animals could be described. His mountain was, in effect, a map set up on end, with various "life zones" succeeding each other from the desert upward, like broad belts circling the mountain.

From this concept, Merriam developed a new system for categorizing plants and animals, based not on geographical areas but on regions of characteristic temperature and humidity. These two, he wrote, "are the most important causes governing distribution and . . . temperature is more potent than humidity." He divided the mountain and its environs into seven zones: the Alpine at the summit; the sub-Alpine at the timberline; the Hudsonian in the area of the spruce forests; the Canadian in the area of the Douglas fir; the Neutral Zone, where the ponderosa pines began; the Piñon Pine Zone; and finally, the Desert Zone. Since the first four zones had certain northern influences in common, he lumped them into a major category, the Boreal Division. The last two zones being definitely southern he put together in the Sonoran Division, and the Neutral Zone was later to become known as the Transition Zone, where northern influences blended into southern.

Merriam's concept of "life zones" was subsequently extended to include all of North America. Spread out on a map, they would look like a series of broad, irregular belts marked by lines of equal temperature running principally east and west in their broad outlines but with large areas appearing as islands or peninsulas where one zone, higher or lower than the surrounding territory, intrudes upon another. For more than a generation every regional bird book published in the U.S. followed Merriam's terminology in describing the ranges of birds. Thus we learned that the black-throated green warbler breeds chiefly in the Canadian and Transition Zones, relatively northern or high regions of conifers, while the cactus wren breeds mainly in the Lower Sonoran Zone.

Today Merriam's system has fallen into disuse because botanists pointed out that he based too much on temperature and that his use of isothermal lines running from east to west was often illogical. Instead, they devised the biome concept based on the major landscape units, such as grasslands, deciduous forest, coniferous forest, tundra, desert and so on, with a broad blend zone, or ecotone, between each major area. Following this system, the aspen groves of the western foothills, for instance, become the ecotone between the grassland biome and the coniferous forest biome.

Within the biome there are smaller areas, or developmental stages, which, in time, if left alone will again assume the major characteristics of the biome. For example, if a conifer forest is burned, it grows back at first into bracken and low brush, then into aspen and birch and finally into conifers again. The aspen and birch, however, although they are deciduous trees, are not part of the deciduous biome, but rather a developmental stage of the coniferous biome.

All of these concepts have their logic and their applicability to plant and animal life, but none of them entirely satisfies the ornithologist's desire to fit birds into a coherent distribution pattern. In the burned conifer forest mentioned above, redstarts and red-eyed vireos will nest for a while in the aspen and birch, but that does not mean that they belong to that biome or even to that one life zone. The thing that is important to them is second growth deciduous trees; whether they be aspen and birch or not, that is where they find their niche.

THE horned lark shows a similar disregard of zones. In North America it is to be found in summer from the dry Mexican tablelands to the arctic tundra, while in the Old World it nests spottily from the North African deserts to the edge of the arctic sea. Considered merely geographically, or even from the biome or life zone concepts, this is a confusing distribution indeed—but the important thing to a horned lark is broad expanses of short grass, be they desert grasslands, plains or tundra. In Audubon's day breeding larks had not yet invaded the wooded northeast, but today they nest from Virginia to New England, where their favorite habitats are golf courses and airports—man-made "prairies."

There are cases, however, where birds of the same species occupy totally different environments in various parts of their ranges. The common raven, one of the most widely distributed birds in the Northern Hemisphere, lives in such dissimilar terrain as the waterless Sahara, the coniferous forests of Canada and Siberia, the sea cliffs of western North America and Scandinavia and the tundra

WESTERN FLYCATCHER 8,000 FEET (2,400 M)

COUES' FLYCATCHER 7,000 FEET (2,100 M)

OLIVACEOUS FLYCATCHER 6,000 FEET (1,800 M)

ASH-THROATED FLYCATCHER 5,000 FEET (1,500 M)

WIED'S CRESTED FLYCATCHER 4,000 FEET (1,200 M)

VERMILION FLYCATCHER 3,000 FEET (900 M)

SPECIFIC SPOTS FOR SPECIFIC BIRDS

Bird distribution is closely tied to food. This is most clearly shown on a mountainside where different bird species tend to sort themselves into zones matching the bands of vegetation. On a typical mountain in southern Arizona (left), several species of flycatchers may be found. On the plain at its base, the vermilion flycatcher flits among streamside cottonwood trees, and is followed by the Wied's crested flycatcher on the low slopes, where giant cactus replaces the trees. Going up the slope, a new species is dominant about every thousand feet, ending with the western flycatcher among the fir and aspen near the top.

and the islands of the arctic sea. The common denominator, if there is one at all, seems to be wilderness.

The fact is that although some birds can be made to fit the life zone concept or the biome concept, both systems are an oversimplification that tends to ignore the evidence of evolutionary processes. Nature is dynamic, defying neat pigeon-holing. Each species, to survive, must be able to exploit a niche just a bit different from that of its neighbors. If the ranges of all 9,000 bird species were plotted on one great world map, their boundaries would seldom coincide, except on some islands, nor would their habitats be precisely the same. The resulting map would be as diffuse as a rainbow.

W HAT is the world population of birds? James Fisher, the British ornithologist, estimated that the number is in the order of 100 billion. My estimate for the United States, made some years ago, was that there are not less than five billion breeding land birds and probably closer to six billion at early summer, or two and a half to three birds per acre (0.4 ha). This was based on the breeding-bird censuses of the National Audubon Society, which use singing males on territory as an index to the number of pairs per acre in different types of terrain. Naturalist Leonard Wing, using a more complicated formula than my rather rough mathematics, came up with a summer population estimate of about 5.6 billion. Neither of these estimates, which might better be called guesstimates, has been challenged since we made them in the 1940s, although I now think they may be a bit high. Both estimates were for the United States south of the Canadian border and did not include Canada and Alaska, a combined area more than 140 per cent as large as the United States. Within the area of Canada and Alaska an equally large population must be resident during the summer months. Add to this an average of two young birds successfully fledged for each pair and we have a late summer figure for North America north of Mexico that may be as high as 20 billion. In light of this, Fisher's estimate of 100 billion for all the continents seems reasonable.

Just how many hundreds of millions or billions of sea birds roam the seven seas is anyone's guess, but although they comprise only three per cent of the

A GROWING FOREST AND ITS CHANGING BIRDS

It is the same rock in all five of these pictures, but they span more than 50 years—the time it may take an open meadow to return to mature forest. At each stage of its development the landscape attracts different birds. In the first scene, a meadowlark has found the abundance of grass and open space that it needs. In the second, the meadowlark has departed; short, woody plants have taken root and a song sparrow has moved in. In the third, more bushes and saplings appear and with them the brush-loving indigo bunting, replacing the song sparrow. In scene four a young, or second-growth, forest has become established along with birds like the redstart, which gleans insects from the leaves. In the last picture the forest is mature and some of the trees are dying, prey to wood-boring insects that attract woodpeckers.

MEADOWLARK   **SONG SPARROW**

world's bird species they probably make up more than three per cent of the total population. Their way of life is a demanding one, but they have few predators and they live for a long time. The period of basic training itself is relatively long. Unlike land birds, which may breed at the age of a year, most sea birds must wait several years before they are sufficiently adept at navigating the sea and wresting a living from it to be able to feed mouths other than their own. A royal albatross may be nine years out of the parental nest before it again touches land and reproduces for the first time. It takes this long to master the art of being an albatross, which, as Fisher said, is probably the most exacting occupation in the bird world. And not only do many sea birds delay their first nesting for a considerable period, but when they do breed they lay relatively small clutches of eggs. Albatrosses, petrels, shearwaters, sooty terns, tropic birds, most auks and many of the other truly pelagic birds lay only one egg, but this single egg is enough to maintain their population level.

IN fact, some of the world's most abundant birds are oceanic. Darwin wrote that he believed the northern fulmar (a gull-like petrel) to be the commonest bird in the world. Fisher, a world authority on the fulmar, disagreed: Although there may be several millions of fulmars, he stated, there are certainly not hundreds of millions. He suggested that the most abundant sea bird may well be Wilson's petrel, a swallow-sized storm-petrel that makes the journey to the north Atlantic every summer from its breeding grounds at the edge of the Antarctic. Also enormously abundant are many of the shearwaters, which look like small, tube-nosed gulls. A single flock of short-tailed shearwaters off Bass Strait, Australia, was once computed to number more than 150 million birds.

Penguin colonies often number into the hundreds of thousands and an aggregation of five million Adélie penguins has been recorded in a single group of islands. Sooty tern colonies on islands in the Indian Ocean have been reported to exceed a million birds and many colonies of auks in arctic and subarctic waters surpass that figure. No one knows how many dovekies or little auks live on the inaccessible cliffs of Greenland, Iceland and Spitsbergen. Certainly millions, and the Atlantic puffin, a relative of the little auk, has been estimated to

INDIGO BUNTING   **REDSTART**   **HAIRY WOODPECKER**

number roughly 15 million. Undoubtedly the largest, single bird city in North America, with perhaps several million birds of a dozen species, is on the great cliffs of Staraya Artil on the island of St. George in the Pribilofs. But even this aggregation is outnumbered by the guano birds—perhaps more than 10 million strong—on the islands off the desert coast of Peru.

Finland is one of the very few countries with a fairly accurate estimate of its total bird population. The Finnish ornithologist Einari Merikalio boldly attempted to evaluate his country's avifauna by using a technique called the line strip method. Each year during June and early July for 15 years, from 1941 to 1956, he made daily transects of the countryside, following a track which formed an enclosed square exactly one kilometer on each side. Each bird seen or heard was duly noted. His researches carried him into every corner of the country, from the Gulf of Finland to the arctic, and indicated not only that there were approximately 64 million birds in Finland, or about 1.3 birds per acre (0.4 ha), but the approximate number of each species.

In Great Britain one gets the impression of many birds because of the relative abundance of the birds of garden and roadside. Actually, the total number of breeding land birds in England, Scotland and Wales has been estimated to be in the neighborhood of 120 million—slightly over two birds per acre. This figure was arrived at by counting the birds in sample acreages of different environments, using the singing male method. Although gardens and estates in England often average 30 birds per acre, extensive grass country and moorland, with less than one bird per acre, pull the average down.

In the United States the greatest density of nesting land birds is undoubtedly in the colonies of the tricolored blackbird in California, a bird very much like the familiar red-winged blackbird, except that it is highly colonial. Tricolored blackbird colonies may harbor as many as 200,000 pairs and may average between 5,000 and 10,000 nests per acre.

If we are to rule out colonial birds, densities of nesting land birds, in the United States, as documented by the Audubon Breeding Bird Census, run from less than one bird per acre on prairies and short-grass plains to 15 or 16 in some rich bogs, swamp-bordered islands and southern hardwood forests. It is quite likely that some marshes support even higher densities, as do suburban estates where the birds have been built up by artificial feeding, nest boxes and berry-bearing shrubs. The average healthy woodland harbors four or five nesting birds per acre, but a wood that has been stripped of its undergrowth by browsing animals may support less than one bird per acre.

Early in the 20th Century, Wells Cook of the U.S. Department of Agriculture made an extensive survey of the bird populations in rural country. His findings showed that U.S. farms averaged about two birds per acre. If we are to assume that there are about 1,124,000,000 acres (455 million ha) of farmland in the United States, including croplands, pasturelands and farm wood lots, the birds would number about 2.25 billion, more than one third the total bird population in the country. However, after Cook published his report, the use of chemical pesticides, many of them lethal to bird life, increased enormously, and over large sections of farmland many birds succumbed.

The tropics, rich in variety, seem to support more birds acre by acre than northern regions. Few tropical censuses have been taken except in Mexico, but it is my impression that in some of the scrub-covered grasslands in East Africa, particularly in southern Kenya, densities might well exceed 40 birds per acre.

Not every acre (0.4 ha) of land is blessed with nesting birds; we have been speaking of averages. Away from the polar icecaps, perhaps the largest areas of birdless country are such lifeless stretches as the Atacama Desert in Chile, lying between the coast and the high Andes, a 600-mile-long (970-km) wasteland as sterile as an operating table. In the United States the Bonneville salt flats west of Great Salt Lake in Utah are certainly the largest birdless area.

Where would the world's highest density be? In the flamingo concentrations of the Rift Valley in Kenya and Tanzania it is not exceptional to observe more than a million lesser flamingos feeding together in one tight-packed, milling mass. But terns, cormorants and auks take up less space than flamingos. At Isla Raza in the Gulf of California 40,000 elegant terns may nest on a single acre; many eggs are but nine inches (23 cm) apart. Among land birds, the swarming colonies of queleas, or locust birds, in Africa defy description. These tiny weaver finches, which may gather in flocks of a million or more, recall tales of the passenger pigeons; they are so numerous that they darken the sky and break large limbs of trees when they settle. Farmers regard them as an agricultural menace and fight them with flame throwers and explosives.

What is North America's number one bird? Is it the house sparrow, introduced from England? Almost certainly not; the starling, less restricted to cities and farms, now outnumbers it. The American robin, however, is a more likely candidate than either. From coast to coast it inhabits cities and forests alike and is one of the most abundant birds in the vast, 3,000-mile (4,800-km) conifer belt stretching across Canada to Alaska. Recently it has been suggested that the red-winged blackbird may be the most numerous bird south of the Canadian border. Nesting not only in every state but probably in every county, it seems to be having a population explosion. Winter roosts often number in the millions.

WHAT are the rarest North American birds? Two are so close to the void of extinction that their existence has been questioned in recent years. The Eskimo curlew, a shore bird with a slender curved bill, was once abundant on the American plains during its passage from the Argentine to the Arctic. Killed off for sport and for food before shore birds were removed from the game list, it went unrecorded for a number of years. However, in April 1959, a single bird appeared at Galveston Island on the coast of Texas and one was seen there during each of the following two springs. In 1962 there were two. In 1974 two were seen in Martha's Vineyard, and one was sighted at North Point, Ontario, in 1976.

The unadaptable ivory-billed woodpecker, North America's largest woodpecker, has not been recorded with certainty since the 1950s, but reports of it still persist and it is just possible that some are valid. The Everglade kite, a snail-eating hawk of the Okeechobee region of Florida, numbers about a hundred now, the last of the species in the United States. From southern Mexico to Argentina, however, it is still common; it is even possible to see a hundred in a day's drive south of Buenos Aires.

In 1977 there were some 110 whooping cranes in the world, including 26 in captivity. Each autumn the eyes of two nations, Canada and the United States, are on the small surviving company of wild whoopers as the cranes make the lengthy and hazardous journey between their only known nesting area, in Wood Buffalo Park in northern Alberta, to their wintering ground on the coast of Texas. In 1941, its blackest year, this species was at an all-time low of 15, and only massive efforts at preservation prevented its extinction.

THE EDGE OF EXTINCTION

ESKIMO CURLEW

The Eskimo curlew was hunted with such greed along the whole length of its migratory route, from the Canadian tundra south to Argentina, that by 1925 it was reported extinct. Several individuals have been sighted in Texas, however, since 1959.

IVORY-BILLED WOODPECKER

North America's rarest bird, if indeed it is still extant, the ivory-billed woodpecker may number a few individuals in the southern United States. To survive, it needs large stands of virgin timber—and the primeval forests are virtually gone.

Next on the list is the California condor, the North American bird with the greatest wing span. Living in the rugged coast range north and west of Los Angeles, it has maintained a population of around 40 in recent decades.

There are probably no more than 50 species of birds whose world populations are known. Birds that are rare and conspicuous, such as cranes and condors, can sometimes be counted beak by beak. Sea birds restricted to single colonies on islands can also be assessed. Reports from the Galápagos Islands, for example, indicate that there are at least 2,000 pairs of Galápagos albatrosses on Hood Island, exclusive of those at sea; about 500 flightless cormorants on Albemarle and Narborough, and perhaps a similar number of Galápagos penguins.

Game birds and species of economic importance are often intensively surveyed. For example, the U.S. Fish and Wildlife Service, in cooperation with other organizations, periodically counts the number of lesser sandhill cranes, a species that is hunted in certain places. In 1977 there were an estimated 300,000, and hunting was not endangering their numbers.

THE only songbird whose continental population is accurately known is Kirtland's warbler, which is restricted to jack-pine forests in about six counties in Michigan. In 1953, Harold Mayfield and his associates counted this gray-backed, yellow-breasted bird and were confident that the number was very close to 1,000. However, by 1976, the population had dropped to only 400. But going from such local ranges to continental distribution is difficult. While we know that there are about 10 million chaffinches in Great Britain and 10.6 million in Finland, these birds are also found from North Africa to central Asia, and it would take an army of census takers to sample their whole range. A rash guess at the chaffinch's world population? More than 200 million.

Territory, the area defended by individual birds, is an important concept in understanding bird populations. Homeowners often report robins, cardinals or other birds buffeting against their windows. These misguided creatures apparently mistake their reflections in the glass for other birds of their kind and are bent on driving them away. Each male is a property owner, a status seeker. By holding territory, birds space themselves out, assuring themselves of a stable food supply during the critical nesting period. They do not sing for the joy of singing so much as to proclaim property rights. Song is a challenge to rivals: "This is my land—keep off!"

Birds, then, tend to limit their own numbers. The unemployed birds wander widely and are kept on the move by the more successful males, who see them off with a song and a brisk flurry if necessary. If by some chance a predator catches one of the established males, his place is quickly filled by the next free-lancing prospector. To determine the extent of this replacement, biologists of the U.S. Fish and Wildlife Service in a drastic but useful experiment tried to kill all the males in a 40-acre (16-ha) forest in Maine. Other males moved in to take their places and although these too were killed the number that came in the following year was nearly the same as before. Nature, like a bank, keeps a surplus to cover losses. Conversely, shooting hawks or foxes or even cats will not result in more birds, for in the absence of predators other natural checks will act as levelers—catastrophes during migration or bad weather, disease, parasites, starvation, or perhaps most effective of all, the birds themselves, practicing birth control through their tradition of defending territory. Consider for a moment what would happen if these checks did not exist. If a single pair of robins holding down a territory of an acre and a half (0.6 ha) succeeded in the spring of 1970 in raising its two broods of four young, there would be 10 robins by the end of the season. This could happen. But suppose this pair and their progeny escaped all the problems that robins are heir to, had 100 per cent success with their families and all of their descendants survived year after year.

By the end of 10 years (the possible life span of the first pair), in the spring of 1980, there would be 19,531,250 robins instead of two—nearly 300 robins for every square foot (0.1 m^2) of the acre and a half!

Agriculturists often debate whether birds really control insects. Undeniably, poison sprays are temporarily more efficient; birds do not do the complete job. But birds working in concert with predatory insects and parasites keep most insect populations in some sort of equilibrium. However, during epidemic outbreaks of certain insects the birds, though prospering, cannot reduce the eruption to a normal level. In a Canadian forest suffering from an outbreak of spruce budworm, nesting warblers may build up to an extraordinary density. During one such outbreak S. Charles Kendeigh recorded that in one area 88 pairs of bay-breasted warblers alone had territories averaging scarcely more than a third of an acre (0.1 ha) in extent.

Insect boom is followed by insect bust. Starvation, not predation by the birds, seems to be the main factor that brings things into line again—starvation when the insects have eaten themselves out of house and home. The birds, at peak abundance because of their earlier nesting success, are now hard put to find food. Unless they can find other food somewhere, their numbers, too, may go into a sharp decline.

It is quite likely that more birds have cyclic ups and downs than we recognize. We witness the irregular movements of some of the boreal Canadian birds —crossbills, pine grosbeaks, redpolls, Bohemian waxwings and others. Some winters they visit the northern United States in great flocks, quickening the pulse of the field-glass fraternity; then for several years we do not see them, nor can we predict the next invasion. We cannot seem to fit them into a cyclic pattern; they are irruptive. On the other hand, the northern shrike, a songbird that preys on mice, seems to be tied in with the four-year vole cycle. When these mice crash, which often coincides with the lemming crash, the shrikes leave their open subarctic forest and are to be seen in considerable numbers in the northern United States.

B ECAUSE grouse are important game species, sportsmen have long known of their fluctuations. In North America the ruffed grouse has a cycle that varies from nine to 11 years. The red grouse of Britain is more irregular; its cycle may be three to 10 years. In Scandinavia the willow ptarmigan, a grouse that goes white in winter, has a three- to four-year cycle.

The famous lemming cycle averages four years, varying between three and five, and when these little arctic rodents build up to a point where they start their suicidal wanderings, the snowy owls, the rough-legged hawks and all the other mouse-eating predators wax fat and raise large broods. But then, at just about the time these birds reach their peak, the lemmings go into a population tailspin. The snowy owls, which in other years stay in the far north, are then forced to wander in search of other food. Many reach the northern United States, particularly along the Atlantic coast, around the Great Lakes and on the northern prairies. During one particularly great flight in the winter

CALIFORNIA CONDOR

For the California condor, the largest of all North American vultures, the change from ranches to fruit farms and then to suburbs has resulted in a diminishing supply of the carrion on which it feeds. The surviving birds—40 or so—are protected but they seem unable to reproduce.

NÉNÉ

Although the inroads of man reduced the néné, or Hawaiian goose, population to a low point of 25 in 1949, the birds are making a comeback. They are being bred in captivity and reintroduced into the wild, where it is estimated that 1,000 of the birds were living in 1977.

of 1945 and 1946, there were 13,502 reports of these big, white owls filed by ornithologists from southern Canada and the northern United States.

The goshawk, a powerful predator of the Canadian forest, is linked with the 10-year cycle of the varying hare and ruffed grouse. In the years when it is forced to travel south it turns its attentions to cottontails and pheasants.

Although voles are apparently not cyclic in Britain, there is on record a great plague of voles on the Scottish border in 1891 and 1892. Short-eared owls moved in and capitalized on the situation by raising exceptionally large broods of 8 to 10 young. Their abnormally extended breeding season, from February to July, suggests that some had more than one brood. When the voles crashed, the owls moved out, but many were found dead of starvation. A similar situation existed in Scotland in 1952 and 1953.

The ranges of birds are not static. Contrast the limited domains today of the California condor, the whooping crane, the swallow-tailed kite and the trumpeter swan with their ranges of a hundred years ago. On the other hand, birds of central Europe gained a foothold in Scandinavia during the first half of the 20th Century and no less than nine continental species established themselves in Iceland. Similarly, on our own continent, cardinals, Carolina wrens, tufted titmice and other "southern" birds have expanded northward into the New England states in recent years.

Occasionally, wind-drifted strays consolidate a beachhead far from home. In January 1937, a number of fieldfares from Norway were carried on a high wind to Greenland, where they manage to survive to this day in the birch groves of fiords near the southern tip. Had they encountered their New World relative, the American robin, which does not live in Greenland, it is unlikely that the fieldfares would have withstood the competition. Less fortunate were some 1,000 lapwings that made the crossing from Ireland to Newfoundland in 24 hours during a strong easterly gale in 1927. They all perished because of the winter weather. It is likely that most such wanderers die, although all oceanic islands where land birds exist must have been populated originally by strays.

THE most successful invaders in recent times have usually had some assist by man—the starling, the house sparrow, not to mention some of the transplanted game species. However, no one knows how the cattle egret of Africa made the jump from the Old World to the New. It arrived, undetected at first among the other white herons, in British Guiana (now Guyana), to be first noticed in the late 1930s. In 1952 it appeared on the Atlantic seaboard of the United States. By 1962 the bird was breeding as far north as New Jersey and Ontario, and roosts of as many as 30,000 were reported in Florida. This is certainly the most spectacular bird invasion in our time.

Thus the bird population, locally as well as on a worldwide scale, is in subtle but constant flux. One winter, cardinals may flock around feeding stations in Connecticut bringing delight to suburban homeowners; the next year a glimpse of them may be a rarity. An influx of a new and different species may cause bird watchers in one locality to go scrambling for their binoculars and record books, while elsewhere a long stable population will be on the wane. It is just this that makes birds so endlessly fascinating to all who have ever given them more than cursory attention: As great as is the pleasure of recognizing old friends as the seasons change, the constant expectation of meeting new ones is a greater pleasure still.

A FLOCK OF KNOTS, MIGRATING SOUTH FROM THE ARCTIC, RESTS ON THE ENGLISH COAST. THEY MAY FLY AS FAR AS WEST AFRICA

100,000,000,000 Birds

From polar icecaps to humid jungles, the world's billions of birds extract a living from almost every kind of environment. In the tropics the rich variety of food gives rise to an amazing variety of species. By contrast, the colder regions support only a few, but these, mostly sea birds that feed on the hordes of fish abounding in icy currents, frequently live in crowded colonies of millions.

A Census of Species

ALASKA 324 / 222
YUKON 178 / 126
NORTHWEST TERRITORIES 266 / 182
GREENLAND 196 / 58
BRITISH COLUMBIA 384 / 276
ALBERTA 317 / 246
SASKATCHEWAN 316
MANITOBA 319 / 245
ONTARIO 366 / 267
LABRADOR 162 / 88
QUEBEC 328 / 228
NEWFOUNDLAND 260 / 128
PRINCE EDWARD ISLAND 222 / 103
WASHINGTON 350 / 235
OREGON 360 / 232
IDAHO 300
MONTANA 335 / 224
NORTH DAKOTA 307 / 171
MINNESOTA 358 / 224
WISCONSIN 350 / 203
MICHIGAN 333 / 202
NEW YORK 412 / 220
MAINE 350 / 176
NOVA SCOTIA 313 / 160
NEW BRUNSWICK 316 / 166
NEW HAMPSHIRE 340 / 175
VERMONT 310 / 175
MASSACHUSETTS 400+ / 177
RHODE ISLAND 333 / 141
CONNECTICUT 347 / 158
NEW JERSEY 387 / 181
DELAWARE 334 / 160
MARYLAND 346 / 192
NEVADA 322
UTAH 325 / 220
WYOMING 343 / 222
SOUTH DAKOTA 340 / 207
NEBRASKA 388 / 194
IOWA 361 / 154
ILLINOIS 360 / 160
IND. 321 / 151
OHIO 340 / 180
PENNA. 340 / 185
W. VA. 293 / 156
VIRGINIA 365 / 179
CALIFORNIA 461 / 286
ARIZONA 433 / 246
NEW MEXICO 400 / 247
COLORADO 430 / 235
KANSAS 380 / 175
MISSOURI 370 / 175
KENTUCKY 312 / 153
NORTH CAROLINA 357 / 178
OKLAHOMA 400+ / 180
ARKANSAS 310 / 130
TENNESSEE 306 / 160
S. CAROLINA 368 / 152
GEORGIA 340 / 160
TEXAS 545 / 300
LOUISIANA 395 / 158
MISS 323 / 130
ALABAMA 350 / 145
FLORIDA 405 / 160
MEXICO 970 / 750
HAWAII 171 (including 14 extinct) / 80

U.S. south of CANADA 725 / 535
U.S. including ALASKA and HAWAII 840 / 695
North America, north of MEXICO 775 / 650
CANADA 520 / 414
WEST INDIES 493 / 300

Shown on these two maps are regional censuses of birds by species in North America and Europe. This recent breakdown by state, province and country is the first published attempt to present such an overall survey. Its population figures were obtained from approximately 100 of the world's leading ornithologists. The black figure in each case represents the total number of species known to have been observed in each area. This figure includes permanent residents, summer and winter visitors, migrants and occasional or accidental visitors from other areas. The

ICELAND
231
76

ALL EUROPE (EXCLUSIVE OF U.S.S.R.) 577 420

FINLAND
328
203

SWEDEN
356
240

NORWAY
333
220

U.S.S.R.
704
622

JAPAN 425 218
INDIA 1,125 920
CHINA (including Tibet) 1,100
KOREA 360
OUTER MONGOLIA 300

DENMARK 341 183
HOLLAND 364 184
BELGIUM 343 148

IRELAND
338
133

GREAT BRITAIN
(England, Scotland, and Wales)
440
190

POLAND
370
230

GERMANY
435
250

CZECHOSLOVAKIA
300
190

ROMANIA
345
240

AUSTRIA
338
215

HUNGARY
332
185

FRANCE
441
260

SWITZ.
347
186

YUGOSLAVIA
236

BULGARIA
338
236

ITALY
450
232

PORT.
315
180

SPAIN
397
225

GREECE
339
204

colored figure represents the number of species that have been recorded as breeding.

No fossils or subspecies are included in these totals, but they do include foreign species successfully introduced as well as a few species that have become extinct in recent times.

No record has been included that is not based on a collected specimen, a recognizable photograph or a well-documented sight record by at least two competent observers. In cases where a figure is missing, such as the total number of species that have been reported in Yugoslavia or the number that breed in Idaho, it was left out because no figure was available at this time.

All these totals are approximate. They will inevitably grow as more and more species are recorded by more observers. For areas such as Great Britain, Massachusetts and New York, the figures may seem a bit inflated—reflecting the work of armies of bird watchers who have been studying those areas for many years. Today their chance of finding new birds, though not remote, is diminishing.

A COLONY OF MURRES NESTS ATOP A ROCKY PINNACLE OFF THE BRITISH COAST AS KITTIWAKE GULLS BREED ON THE LOWER LEDGES

Rigors and Rewards of a Crowded Life

Birds colonize for different reasons. They may be naturally gregarious. They may be gaining protection from predators, conserving body heat in a cold climate, exploiting the neighborhood's food supply, or any combination of these things. A scarcity of nesting places may force birds into a communal life, sometimes even with other species, on the few good sites that are available. This is true of the murres, the weak-winged northern counterparts of the flightless penguins.

Murres colonize for still another reason: To mate and breed successfully, they need to be stimulated by the noisy encouragement of a crowd. Thus, they are found in tightly packed and exuberant masses on the cliffs and pinnacles of islands on rocky northern coasts, thousands nesting together, each almost a pecking distance apart from its neighbors. Those who start to breed first form the center of the colony, where they are safest from the raids of predators. When a young murre is nearly three weeks out of the egg and its wings are still only half grown, it becomes restless and, with only a little parental urging, jumps off the cliff and begins to fend for itself.

Much of the murres' pattern of life is duplicated by the penguins in the bottom half of the world because both birds have been molded by similar environments and similar problems in making a living. Like the murres, penguins go back to the same breeding ground year after year; some species help raise each other's young in nurseries. But there is a maverick colony of penguins too: Though most people associate these natty birds with the cold wastes of the antarctic ice, a colony of about 250 lives in the Galápagos Islands, on the equator.

SPLASHING IN THE SURF, Magellanic penguins scurry away from the photographer who has discovered their colony in the Straits of Magellan. Unlike the murres of northern coasts, which nest only on rocky cliffs and pinnacles, Magellanic penguins will live on almost any kind of coast—scrub, rain forest or grassy moor—as long as it is suitable for digging their burrow nests.

The Biggest Bird Colony

Food is one of the most important single reasons why birds form colonies, and food is the dominating factor in the biggest bird colony on earth. Its inhabitants, some 10 million strong, are the piqueros and guanay cormorants that live on the hot, arid islands off the coast of Peru. They feast on the billions of anchovies in the cold Humboldt Current just offshore, and the droppings from this rich diet form the finest natural fertilizer in the world—guano.

The guano birds' harvesting of the anchovies is systematic and endless. After small squadrons have searched the sea for schools of fish, the birds attack in force. Thousands at a time hiss into the sea like spears, vanishing in a geyser of foam. Again and again they dive until at last, darkening the sky, they return to their island homes. Their colonies are so crowded, at about three families to the square meter, that government wardens can count the population by simply measuring a colony's dimensions.

The unique value of the guano colonies as fertilizer factories has been recognized for more than 1,000 years, and the birds themselves were placed under strict protection by the Incas. Later, however, they were so severely exploited that in 1909 Peru was forced to set up a guano administration to regulate the harvesting and, once again, protect the birds.

SACKS OF GUANO are stacked in rows by squads of workers on a Peruvian coastal island. By government law, the removals of guano may not exceed the amounts left annually by the birds.

PLUMAGE GLEAMING, boobies nest on South Guañape Island in Peru. Building up about six inches (15 cm) of guano a century, birds have created deposits as deep as 150 feet (46 m).

A STARTLED SKYFUL of flamingos shatters the stillness of the morning above their native Camargue, a desolate land of brackish swamps and salt flats in the estuaries of the Rhone River. Long hunted for its plumage, this shy and beautiful bird is now protected in its remote mud cities by the French government. Mating, nest building, incubating the egg, feeding the young—

everything that a flamingo does in its life, it does in large colonies. While it is true that this need for community living is exhibited by birds at all levels, ornithologists have found that it is particularly true of large birds on the lower rungs of the evolutionary ladder, where the instinctive drives seem to be reinforced by the sight of thousands of others acting the same way.

HAPHAZARD MIGRANTS, hardy evening grosbeaks do not go south when winter comes as long as berries and other food are available. Only when food runs short do they wander, often eastward to the Atlantic states.

5

The Riddle of Migration

SINCE first he watched the flight of birds, man has pondered their disappearance in the fall and their reappearance in the spring. A passage in the Bible (Jeremiah 8:7) notes the regularity of these comings and goings: "Yea, the stork in the heaven knoweth her appointed times; and the turtle [dove] and the crane and the swallow observe the time of their coming."

It was a most intriguing mystery and a number of different answers were offered. Aristotle, the foremost naturalist of antiquity, acknowledged that some birds migrate, "as in the case of the crane," but, he asserted, "they do not all migrate, as is generally supposed, to warmer countries.... The stork, the ouzel, the turtle dove, the lark, all go into hiding." Aristotle also introduced a third possibility—that of transmutation. He announced unequivocally that the European robin underwent a change at the approach of summer and became the European redstart.

For 2,000 years these ancient pronouncements were repeated by countless authors who elaborated on the writings of their predecessors without examining nature firsthand. Down through the centuries the ingenuity of people in explaining the seasonal avicycle reached new heights of fancy. Migration was now accepted in the case of many of the big birds, but the tiny birds, naturalists rationalized, got across the oceans by hitching rides on the backs of their larger fellows. Still later, the most bizarre theory of all was published, perhaps tongue in cheek, in 1703 by an Englishman who described himself as "a person of learning and piety." He wrote that birds flew to the moon, taking 60 days to get there and that on arrival, finding no nourishment, they went into hibernation!

It seems inconceivable that Linnaeus, who devised the modern system of zoological nomenclature, should have written in his *Systema Naturae* in 1735 that the house martin "lives under the roof in European houses; it is immersed during the winter but comes out in the spring."

THE ghost of bird hibernation had finally been laid to rest—or so everybody thought for a century—when, in December 1946, Dr. Edmund C. Jaeger and two companions, exploring a canyon in the Chuckawalla Mountains in southeastern California, discovered a poorwill, a small night bird of the whippoorwill type, tucked into a rocky crevice. Suspecting it to be dead, they were surprised when the bird blinked an eye. They kept it under observation for four successive winters and always the same bird was to be found in deathlike lethargy in the crevice. One winter it remained inactive for 88 days. A series of tests showed that its temperature dropped to 64.6° F. (18.1° C.). (The normal temperature of an active poorwill is about 106° F. [41.1° C.].) A beam of light directed into its eye elicited no response; a mirror held up to its nostrils showed no condensation of moisture; even with a stethoscope, the observers could not detect a heartbeat. Yet when spring temperatures stirred the bird to life, it was seen to fly away.

Torpidity has been observed in captive lesser nighthawks, relatives of the poorwill. Hummingbirds may go into a torpor at night and even on cold days. European swifts have been found in a torpid state in France and whitethroated swifts in a similar comatose condition have been recorded in winter on Slover Mountain in California. But whether such birds have the ability to go from torpor into true hibernation remains to be proved.

The word migration, derived from the Latin *migrare* (to go from one place to another), refers to any traveling. Applied to birds, it usually means a yearly round trip. During the brief arctic summer there is vast elbowroom in the tundra for golden plovers and other shore birds, but during eight or nine months of the year no shore bird could survive there. However, the pampas of Argentina, 8,000 miles (12,900 km) distant, offer a similar living. By traveling, the golden plover enjoys two summers each year and knows not a hint of winter. On the other hand, the willow ptarmigan, the grouse that turns white in winter, stays in the frozen north. It shifts its diet from insects to the buds and twigs of willows and alders. Thus migration seems to be a response to population pressures and seasonal food fluctuations.

Most North American and European species take part in the great pageant of migration. In fact, more than a third of all the world's birds are migratory to some degree and the number of individuals involved runs to the tens of billions. Migration is most pronounced in the Northern Hemisphere, where the much larger land masses are covered seasonally with winter's ice and snow. A considerable number of Eurasian and North American birds cross the equator to spend the winter deep in Africa or South America, but few land birds of the latter two continents reverse the process to pass their nonbreeding season in the Northern Hemisphere. They may journey northward toward the equator, and quite a number do, but the few that cross it continue no great distance.

Among southern sea birds, however, there are several that invade northern oceans. Wilson's petrel leaves its nesting grounds at the edge of the antarctic continent to forage in June, July and August as far north as the Newfoundland banks. Greater shearwaters from remote Tristan da Cunha in the South Atlantic and sooty shearwaters from islands around Cape Horn range to the offshore waters of Greenland. On the other side of the world, the short-tailed shearwater, the "mutton bird" of the Australians, wanders in a great loop through the Pacific, from the Bass Strait off southeast Australia, past Japan to the Bering Sea and back again via the west coast of North America. The extraordinary thing is that the mob—millions of birds—is said to return to the same tiny islands on the same evening in late November.

Migration is the greatest adventure in the life of a bird, the greatest risk it must take. Hundreds of millions of migrants never reach their destination, dying en route in storms or accidents. Despite a keen "weather eye" responsive to cloud conditions and despite a probable sensitivity to barometric pressure as well as to humidity, temperature and wind direction, birds are no more able than human weathermen to predict freak storms or fogs ahead. Strong wind streams cutting across their axis of travel may carry them so far to sea at night that they may be unable to regain the land when they become aware of their plight in the morning. Fog seems to confuse their navigation; on misty nights lights attract them and they often crash into lighthouses, lighted monuments and high buildings. A hazard of man's air age that birds must now contend with are the ceilometers at airports, and birds passing across these slender, vertical beams of light sometimes plunge earthward. At Robins Air Force Base in Georgia it was estimated that 50,000 birds were killed in one night because of a ceilometer beam.

Hurricanes may carry sea birds 2,000 miles (3,200 km) from their home seas and drop them exhausted or dying on unfamiliar shores. Since the peak of the hurricane season coincides with the fall passage of many small migrants to the West Indies, a single storm might account for the loss of millions of lives. Ships entering the windless eye of a tropical storm have found the air filled with small land birds, which landed and sought rest on the decks and rigging.

To collect some of the basic facts about migration, birdbanders in recent times have marked many millions of birds in order to plot their travels. Although falconers had marked their hawks since medieval times so that they could be returned in case of loss, modern birdbanding did not begin until 1740, when Johann Leonhard Frisch of Berlin first tied red strings around the legs of swallows before the autumn migration. The first birdbander in America was John James Audubon. Two of the young phoebes on whose legs he had put silver threads returned the following year.

Today banding (called ringing in Europe) is carried on extensively on all continents, including Antarctica. In the United States and Canada some 2,000 banders take part in a joint operation, marking more than a million birds a year. Roughly 5 per cent of the birds banded are recovered and the data analyzed by computer. Similar programs operate in the Soviet Union, most European countries, Australia, New Zealand, Japan and South Africa.

Young birds are easily banded before they leave the nest, but most banders prefer to work with adults, whose survival is more certain.

The devices for catching them are many. Perhaps the most elaborate is the Heligoland trap, basically a large camouflaged funnel of fine wire into which birds are driven through narrowing corridors to end up at last in a glass-backed collecting chamber. Somewhat similar is the Dutch decoy, a long wire funnel placed over a narrow stream into which inquisitive waterfowl are coaxed by a specially trained dog. In fact, the banders have tried almost everything—hair-fine Japanese mist nets, drugged bait, jack lights, foot snares and a vast array of wire traps baited with food and water.

SOME of the journeys documented by banding are extraordinary. An arctic tern banded as a flightless youngster by Oliver Austin Jr. on the coast of Labrador was picked up 90 days later on the coast of southeast Africa, 9,000 miles (14,500 km) away. Another tern, ringed on the arctic coast of Russia, was retaken off Australia, having traveled at least 14,000 miles (22,500 km).

The golden plover is often cited as a close second for the marathon honors, traveling from the arctic tundra to the pampas of Argentina. The white-rumped sandpiper, however, makes the same fall sea hop from maritime Canada but does not stop in the latitude of the pampas—it continues another 1,000 miles (1,600 km) or more, often to the tip of Tierra del Fuego. Its associate, Baird's sandpiper, makes an equally long journey from the Arctic via the high plains and the high Andes. Their paths may be more than 2,000 miles (3,200 km) apart, one over sea, the other through the interior, but these two sandpipers often end their journey on the same Patagonian beaches.

Among land birds the bobolink has often been called the top migrant, covering 7,000 miles (11,300 km) or more between the clover fields of Canada and the grasslands of Argentina. However, some barn swallows may travel as much as 9,000 miles (14,500 km), for the species breeds as far to the north as Alaska and some individuals reach southern Patagonia. Swallows from Scandinavia may rival their North American relatives by traveling the length of Europe and Africa, a flight of about 8,000 miles (12,900 km).

Every autumn, between September and November, a few birds from North America turn up in Europe. Among these are strong-winged shore birds such as yellowlegs, dowitchers and pectoral, white-rumped and buff-breasted

LONG-DISTANCE FLIERS

ARCTIC TERN

The maps on these two pages show the major itineraries of four well-known migratory birds. The greatest traveler of all, the arctic tern, leaves its northern colonies in late summer for the 10,000-mile (16,000-km) trip to seas near Antarctica. Some go via the Pacific, while others go by the west coast of Europe and Africa and may even stray to the Indian Ocean.

WHITE STORK

Storks summer in Europe but spend the winter in South Africa. Expert gliders, they prefer to ride rising air currents and will fly over water only if they can see land on the other side. Thus they have a problem crossing the Mediterranean. Most solve it by taking the eastern route through Asia Minor—then turning south into Africa. Others cross at Gibraltar.

sandpipers, and also many land birds such as cuckoos, thrushes and warblers. For a long time it was thought that the frailer land birds might have hitchhiked on boats. But though assisted passages on boats have been recorded—a white-throated sparrow aboard a liner outbound from New York once hitched a ride all the way to the Scilly Isles—a better explanation is that they were borne over by violent winds. It has even been suggested that they may have been caught at high altitudes in the jet streams, the powerful winds that sweep from west to east around the globe.

Although we often speak of "routes" and "flyways," there is probably not a single square kilometer of the earth, excluding the polar icecaps, over which birds do not fly. A series of classic experiments made by George H. Lowery Jr. and Robert J. Newman while watching the night flight of birds through telescopes trained on the moon, and more recent observations by radar, confirm without a doubt that most nocturnal migration of small land birds proceeds with the general air flow on a broad front—northward in the spring on warm air masses from the south, southward in the autumn on the cool winds of the north. The night migrants do not mass in flocks or follow narrow paths. However, bird watchers observing migration at dawn see a startlingly different picture, particularly at coastal points. At daybreak, the birds, still moving, may be seen flying at an altitude from about 200 feet (61 m) down to bush-top level and into the wind, as an airplane must do when it comes in for a landing. They are then often in groups and appear to be following definite paths, particularly when bodies of water, unseen at night, funnel them into peninsulas and islands. The field-glass birder often takes these concentration points to be normal "routes" and the disparity between what he sees and what the telescope or radar screen reveals has led to lively controversies over the nature of migration.

Although day migrants may be concentrated by such visual land contours as river valleys, coastlines and ridges, giving the impression that they are following precise routes, much diurnal migration also advances over a broad front. The "flyway" concept is an oversimplification, but the terminology is useful for the waterfowl administrators who, on the basis of the drainage pattern of the North American continent, distinguish between the Atlantic flyway, the Mississippi flyway, the Central flyway and the Pacific flyway. Actually many waterfowl switch from one flyway to another in their travels.

PECTORAL SANDPIPER

BOBOLINK

PECTORAL SANDPIPER

A shore bird that breeds in arctic tundra, the pectoral sandpiper does not lose sight of land as it migrates to its winter home in South America. The main route crosses the Great Plains, though in fall some birds make an arc that hits the Atlantic. This species has spread into Siberia, but the Asian birds still cross over into America before making their fall trip south.

BOBOLINK

A land bird that breeds in North American clover fields, the bobolink migrates to the grasslands of Argentina by island hopping through the Caribbean. The small bobolink colonies in the Northwest shun the most direct route to the south through Mexico; like the pectoral sandpipers in Siberia, they make a detour east to fly with their brothers along the ancestral flyway.

Diurnal migrants have a greater tendency to do their traveling in flocks. Well-organized flocks of ducks, geese and swans (which also travel at night) swarm the continental flyways twice a year. Swallows travel by day in loose companies and assemble to roost at dusk. In the United States and Canada, red-winged blackbirds, grackles and starlings are mainly day migrants, as are robins, waxwings, goldfinches and many other familiar flocking species. Occasionally, however, some of these birds may travel at night.

Many species are only partially migratory. Bluebirds and many blue jays that breed in the northern United States and Canada travel southward to mingle in the southern states with resident bluebirds and blue jays that do not migrate at all. Similarly, in Europe most skylarks and wood larks migrate out of Scandinavia, but others stay through the year in England, where the seasons are more equable.

Flight speeds of birds have been clocked many times, but usually at ground speed, and it has been asserted that birds travel faster when migrating than at other times. The speed of most small birds seldom exceeds 30 mph (48 km/h), although swallows and starlings are much faster. Migrating hawks cruise at 30 to 40 mph (48 to 64 km/h). Most shore birds average 40 to 50 mph (64 to 80 km/h), while many ducks travel at 50 to 60 (80 to 97 km/h).

At such speeds as these, migrating birds may cover several hundreds of miles in a single day or night. It is a routine matter for North American migrants to do more than 500 miles (805 km) nonstop across the Gulf of Mexico, where there are no midway islands. One ruddy turnstone, a member of a cosmopolitan species of shore bird that is banded in Germany, covered 510 miles (821 km) in 25 hours. Blue geese make the 1,700 miles (2,750 km) from James Bay in Canada to coastal Louisiana in 60 hours.

Most routine migration probably takes place within 3,000 feet (900 m) of the earth, although David Lack, using radar to compute the altitude of British night migrants, found that some small land birds travel at 5,000 feet (1,500 m) and may go as high as 14,000 feet (4,300 m). Radar has recorded birds flying at 20,000 feet (6,100 m). Such high flights are understandable in species that routinely fly across the Himalayas and the Andes. Yet those same extremely high altitudes are reported for migrants flying over water, and here the heavy winds, low temperatures and oxygen-thin atmosphere make the birds' choice difficult to understand.

Modern documentation of the astonishing travels of the birds has only deepened the mystery of these seasonal round trips. If the physical feats involved are amazing, the mental feats are even more remarkable. Birds are not noted for their intelligence, yet somehow they know when to leave a winter home for a summer home and when to return—and still more remarkably, how to find their way. Only now are scientists beginning to learn how the birds accomplish their triumphs of timing and navigation.

Birds start migrating at approximately the same time each year. The signal is not simply the advent of warm or cool weather—if it were, midwinter thaws would cause disastrous mistiming. Rather, the departures seem to be governed by a complex interplay of various external stimuli (including weather) with internal biological calendars that enable the birds to tell what season of the year it ought to be.

Among the biological calendars are the endocrine glands, the controls that make male birds sing and females lay eggs. Just before each nesting season and just afterward, birds undergo biological changes associated with reproduction. The endocrine glands become very active. It is during these two periods that most birds migrate, so the periodic activity of the endocrine glands appears to be one of the biological calendars that tell birds when it is time for them to travel.

The connection between the nesting season and migration is easy to understand. The hatching of a new generation causes a population boom and a sudden but more-or-less temporary increase in food demand—a demand that could be satisfied by flight to a region where spring has just brought a more-or-less temporary abundance of food.

Another biological calendar calculates the season from the amount of light available, responding to the increase in the length of day in the spring and the decrease in the fall, which scientists call photoperiodism. It is photoperiodism that helps trigger the activity of the endocrine glands each year. To test whether photoperiodism has any bearing on the urge to migrate, experimenters have subjected laboratory birds to artificial increases and decreases of light simulating seasons different from the natural one. Sure enough, when the day length was increased to correspond with spring, the birds displayed all the outward signs of migratory restlessness. When the test was reversed and the birds were made to believe it was fall, they also showed migratory restlessness. But a third test proved that photoperiodism was probably only one of several stimuli that told birds when it was time to go. In the third test, birds of the same species were kept in an artificial environment for a year, during which the length of day and night was kept at a constant cycle of 12 hours each. Without the lengthening or shortening of days to influence them, the birds still showed migratory restlessness in accord with the natural seasons. Clearly they possessed some other form of internal calendar that—without photoperiodism to affect it—went right on crossing off the days until it was time to fly north or south again.

INTERNAL calendars regulated by external stimuli may prepare the birds for migration, but the exact departure date seems to be set simply by the weather. All other factors may say go, but long-distance migrants normally wait for good flying conditions. Birds need favorable winds to help them on their way because the physiological cost of migration is high. Many migrants operate on the slimmest margin of safety. Each fall the blackpoll warbler, for example, flies nonstop from eastern Canada and New England all the way to South America on a daring course that takes it out into the Atlantic as far as Bermuda in order to catch the northeasterly trade winds to Brazil. After such a long overwater flight, the birds making landfall are sometimes so exhausted that they can be picked up in the hand. They are found to have burned up their entire reserves of fat and part of their flight muscles as well. Exploiting the wind helps to assure them that they will reach their destination. If winds are adverse, they delay migration until the weather is right, and then take advantage of prevailing wind currents along the route.

If migrating birds need assistance from the weather to withstand the physical toll of their long trips, much more do they need good direction. They can ill afford to lose their way. Once the complex biological calendars and external stimuli tell them it is time to migrate, and the weather and winds are right, another intricate set of mechanisms must take over to guide them to their distant destinations. It is the birds' ability to maintain a

NAVIGATION BY THE SUN

To test the possibility that birds used the sun as a compass during migration, Gustav Kramer experimented with starlings during their periods of migratory restlessness. When he caged them in an experimental aviary that was lighted only by the sun (top), he found that the birds fluttered about and soon aligned themselves in the same directions of the compass they would have followed had they been free. But when he used adjustable mirrors to deflect the natural sunlight by 90 degrees, the starlings changed their direction to precisely the same degree.

deliberate course over hundreds or thousands of miles—a mystery of avian navigation—that elicits the greatest wonder. The ancients were content to say that Providence guided the birds. Pigeon fanciers call it instinct. Animal behaviorists have attacked the puzzle with increasing vigor in this century.

In some birds, this navigational ability is easily explained, though still remarkable. Geese, cranes and certain other waterfowl follow a route that they have learned by flying with their parents. They apparently remember visual landmarks and orient by them. How else to explain such journeys as that of Ross's goose, which, migrating southward through the North American plains, makes an abrupt westward turn in the vicinity of Great Falls, Montana, to cross the Rockies?

It is difficult to imagine how migrants that follow a complicated traditional path can store the memory of so many landmarks. But birds that, like the blackpoll warbler, cross great stretches of ocean to remote destinations have no landmarks. Perhaps they follow pathways in the sea that are unrecognizable to man. But a large proportion of migrants fly at night, when land or sea features can be of little value. Moreover, many are young birds making their first journey without the guidance of adults.

Such achievements indicate that most migrating birds possess different capacities for navigation. They must have some ability to sense direction and know instinctively which direction to take to follow the established migration route of their species. But in addition, they must possess an ability to learn to home, or find their way, to specific points—return to a goal from a distant location that may or may not lie along an established migration route.

Homing is best observed in pigeons, which have been selectively bred for the purpose at least since Babylonian times. After a series of flights in the vicinity of their natal lofts, pigeons will return from distant places, sometimes 1,000 miles (1,600 km) away, with astonishing fidelity. Ordinary piloting from visual landmarks does not explain such feats, since the birds frequently are obliged to fly over territory they have never seen before. Critics have suggested that perhaps the birds are able to record in some way all the twists and turns made by the vehicle that transports them and that, returning, they simply retrace these twists and turns. In a test of this hypothesis, pigeons have been transported under heavy sedation; when revived at some distant point and released, they have homed as well as birds that were not drugged. They must have some other way of deducing the direction to places they have learned to consider home.

Wild birds are also remarkably skilled at homing. A European swift transported 155 miles (249 km) got back to its home in four hours. A male Manx shearwater removed to Boston's Logan International Airport flew 3,050 miles (4,908 km) back across the Atlantic, arriving at its burrow on Skokholm Island in Wales $12^1/_2$ days later. But for each registered success hundreds of tagged birds were never seen again. Obviously the capacity is there, but it is not always strong enough to meet every challenge. The numerous reports by bird watchers of strays spotted far from their habitats is evidence of that.

The very fact that some birds' navigational skills break down on occasion makes the details of this phenomenon all the more difficult to understand. For a long time investigations suffered from the notion that there existed a single mechanism that would account for avian navigation. Sight, the primary sense for most birds, seemed the most obvious candidate, but sound, smell and a sensitivity to magnetism or even to the rotation of the earth were all put forward as possibilities.

A cornerstone of present-day research was laid during the 1950s by Germany's Gustav Kramer. In a brilliant experiment he showed that birds that traveled by day orient themselves by the position of the sun. Working with starlings in an elaborate circular contraption with six evenly spaced windows, each revealing a patch of sky, he found that during their migratory restlessness these birds perched with their bodies pointed in the direction they would fly if migrating, i.e., northeast in spring and southwest in fall. He then decided to find out if he could trick the birds into facing in another direction by "moving" the sun. He did this by putting adjustable mirrors outside the windows of the cage. The sunlight was reflected into the cage at a different angle and the birds promptly lined themselves up in accordance with this new position of the sun.

The experiment proved that birds use the sun as a compass. But still unresolved was the question of how birds compensate for the constantly changing position of the sun during the day. Part of an answer to that mystery emerged from a corollary experiment by Klaus Hoffmann, who was working with Kramer. The experiment demonstrated that birds possess a highly accurate sense of time. The sun's position shifts by 15 degrees every hour as it appears to cross the sky from east to west. To take a compass bearing from the sun, a bird would have to know, from an accurate internal clock, what time of day the sun was being seen. A course of 90 degrees from a morning sun would lead in quite a different direction from a course of 90 degrees from an afternoon sun. Researchers put birds through a "clock-shift" experiment, in which the cycle of light and dark was shifted to be earlier or later than local time with the use of artificial lights indoors. They found that the birds' internal clocks could be reset by any amount desired. If birds orienting by the sun believed it to be morning when it was really afternoon, they confused east with west. When birds whose clocks had been shifted were placed in a circular cage outdoors at the period of their spring migratory restlessness, they tried to fly south instead of north.

R EVEALING as these experiments were, they explained nothing about how birds migrate at night. The German scientist E. G. F. Sauer proposed that birds take their night bearings from stars. To prove this idea, he put caged birds in the planetarium at the Mariner's School in Bremen. The birds took their direction from the stars projected on the planetarium dome—and tried to fly off in another direction when the artificial heavens were shifted. It was clear that stars were at least one of the factors involved in night navigation, and it was assumed that birds took their directions from the position of prominent constellations in the night sky. But further experiments by Stephen Emlen of Cornell University, working with night-migrating indigo buntings, proved that the birds were more sophisticated than that.

Emlen placed his buntings in a funnel-shaped cage with a clear plastic top that permitted the birds to see the night sky but not the horizon or any other landmarks. This apparatus made it possible to rotate the cage without the birds' being aware of the shift. Only the heavens would change position. The floor of the cage was an inky pad with blotting paper forming the sloping sides. The migratory preferences of each bird were recorded by its inky footprints on the blotting paper as the bird tried to hop predominantly in one

AND BY THE STARS

By placing warblers in a planetarium during their spring restlessness, E.G.F. Sauer found that night migrants use stars for guidance. When he shone a spring sky on the ceiling the birds faced northwest (top), the direction in which they would normally migrate. When he twisted the star pattern the birds turned too. An autumn experiment (center) gave similar results. But with no stars as guides (bottom) birds faced in all directions. The short lines in these circles indicate movement by a few birds, longer lines by more birds, thick arrows by most of the birds.

direction. Emlen found that young birds deprived of a nightly view of the sky left footprints in random patterns. Experienced birds, on the other hand, appeared to have learned the configurations of the constellations so well in earlier life that they could orient themselves to their proper migratory direction even when parts of the sky were blocked from view.

At first it seemed that the birds took their bearings from these constellations of prominent stars much as they took bearings from the sun, augmented by internal clocks that told them what time they were seeing the stars. But the requirements for stellar navigation are much more demanding. There is only one sun but there are thousands of bright stars, different ones visible above the horizon at different seasons. A nocturnal migrant would have to be able to locate a particular star or constellation consistently and then make allowances for its apparent motion.

Emlen discovered that his buntings were not orienting by the constellations alone but by the movement of the constellations in relation to the North Star. Most people learn that in the Northern Hemisphere they can find north simply by noting the position of the North Star. Birds apparently learn that too. When Emlen tested his birds in a planetarium, he established that they took their bearings from the pattern of stars relative to the North Star and could do so regardless of how much their internal clocks were shifted forward or backward. From this it was apparent that birds could tell which direction was north or south by the movement of stars around the North Star, and they could do so at any time of night without regard to an internal clock.

THE ability of birds to use the sun and stars as compasses therefore was plain. Yet radar tracking of night migrants indicated that birds flew quite accurate courses even through dense cloud layers, when they could see neither the ground nor the heavens—suggesting the existence of yet another back-up system of navigation. At once new life was breathed into an old theory. It had often been suggested in the 19th Century that birds might be able to sense magnetic north, aligning themselves with the earth's magnetic field just as the needle of a compass does. The notion was discredited when it was shown that pigeons homed perfectly well while carrying, strapped to their wings, magnets strong enough to drown the impulses of the earth's magnetic field. This conclusion in turn proved too hasty. The pigeons carrying the magnets had simply relied on their sun compasses and ignored whatever confusing magnetic information they were receiving.

New experiments under heavy overcast by Charles Walcott of State University of New York at Stony Brook, William Keeton of Cornell and others revealed that pigeons without magnets apparently switched to magnetic direction finding; those pigeons with magnets strapped to their backs were unable to navigate as well through the overcast as those whose magnetic sensors were not being garbled.

These experiments suggested that birds can navigate night and day over great distances and in heavy overcasts by using a variety of techniques, body clocks and sensors—most of them little understood. But scientists believe there may be more. Also under investigation, in addition to magnetic sensors, are birds' abilities to use ultraviolet light, very low-pitched sounds, polarized light, barometric-pressure changes, odors, temperature, humidity and the atmospheric electric field. Small as it is, the brain of a bird has turned out to be far more complex and capable than man ever imagined.

A REED BUNTING IS HELD GENTLY BUT FIRMLY IN A MIST NET, HAVING BLUNDERED INTO ITS SILKEN MESH BEFORE REALIZING IT WAS THERE

Mysterious Voyagers

Spring and fall, for longer than recorded time, men have looked up in wonder as clouds of migrating birds darkened the skies. To learn where birds go during these mysterious journeys, men have observed them with binoculars, telescopes, radar and other aircraft tracking devices. In addition, they have brought birds to earth in nets, banded them, and sometimes even daubed them with dye.

RESPONSE TO LIGHT in a feeding experiment indicates that birds orient themselves to a light source. This starling, circled by small food boxes in a cage, quickly learned to face toward a bright movable light to find the box that contained its food. Experimenters reason that a similar response to the sun can be useful to migrating birds in orienting themselves as they fly.

How Birds Find Their Way

How birds can find their way over vast distances with apparent ease is a long-standing mystery that is finally being solved. At one time scientists thought birds might navigate by a kinesthetic sense, remembering their routes by pressure patterns formed in their inner ears. But pioneer migration experiments indicated that a bird's sense of direction was a far more complex combination of sensory tools.

Birds make use of visual landmarks but do not depend solely on them. The first steps toward explaining this fact were made in the 1950s by Gustav Kramer, E. G. F. Sauer and others, who showed that many birds are able to orient themselves, as human beings do, by observing the heavens. Migrant birds that were tested during the day appeared to judge direction by correlating the position of the sun in the sky with the readings of internal biological clocks. At night they seemed to receive directional guidance from the stars, as though they had memorized a star map.

MOVABLE MIRRORS can beam sunlight into this experimental aviary at odd angles, making birds inside act as if the sun were in different positions. The birds adjust themselves accordingly.

AN EXPERIMENT IN HOMING from an aviary in an excavation reveals the importance to carrier pigeons of landmarks in locating their home. Birds raised here below ground could not associate their roost with nearby landmarks. When these pigeons were removed from the loft and released miles away, many flew homeward but could not find their own aviary.

An Array of Navigational Talents

Scientists learned in the 1960s and 1970s that sun compasses and star patterns are only two of many extraordinary tools a migrant bird may use in charting its airborne course. In cloudy weather, when visual guides are useless, some birds also make use of an array of supplementary direction-finding mechanisms.

Among these is an apparent capacity for sensing the direction of the earth's magnetic field and aligning themselves appropriately by means of a built-in compass, which, according to one study, may lie within the bird's eye. Birds also may be able to memorize a home territory's characteristic smell. In addition, some experiments indicate that birds can perceive clues that humans cannot, such as densities of ultraviolet light and angles of polarized light. So many different answers have now been found to the riddle of avian navigation that most scientists today think birds, like men, use many separate techniques in finding their way.

IN A FUNNEL CHAMBER a bird that can see star patterns leaves inky footprints to show the direction it aims for. This bird has repeatedly attempted to continue its flight south.

IN A BALLOON-LOFTED CAGE a bird is sent up to be released at a preset altitude and subsequently followed on radar. This is part of a study of reactions to a range of weather conditions.

IN A CONDITIONING CHAMBER a bird receives a small electric shock during experimental studies of its responses to changes in levels of light and fluctuations in the barometric pressure.

A CROWN OF COILED WIRE attached to a battery surrounds a bird with a magnetic field whose north pole points south. Released in an overcast, the bird will head the wrong way.

RELEASING HOMING PIGEONS from an airport at Bedford, Massachusetts, scientists will follow them by plane to study their flight pattern and habits. This continuous tracking is valuable, but it is difficult to do—a plane flies faster than pigeons, and so must keep doubling back; and it must maintain a quarter-mile (0.4-km) distance or it will frighten the birds.

ALUMINUM BANDS developed by the U.S. Fish and Wildlife Service come in 14 diameters ranging from 0.083 to 0.875 inches (0.2 to 2.2 cm).

The Task of Tracking

Many clever techniques have been devised for use in studying the navigation of birds, from simple leg bands to bird-sized radio transmitters.

The most common process, that of banding, allows a record to be made of a single bird's location at two specific moments: first when the metal band is snapped onto its leg, and again if the bird is recovered—alive or dead—and the leg band is removed and returned. Only about 5 per cent of banded birds ever turn up, but even that proportion of return has yielded valuable information—some of it startling. A lesser yellowlegs flew 1,900 miles (3,050 km) from Cape Cod to Martinique in six days, and an oystercatcher turned up healthy some 28 years after banding.

Because metal bands must be physically recovered before they can be of any use, scientists have also employed colorful dyes *(overleaf)* that can be seen from a distance. But the most accurate method of all those now in use involves tracking birds by radar or trailing them in a helicopter or a plane—frequently with the aid of miniature transmitters that have been attached to the birds.

A BAND IS ATTACHED to the leg of a pintail duck as it lies quietly in the arms of a wildlife agent. About 45,000 pintails are now banded annually.

TAGGING SNOW GEESE, agents take bands from a spiked stand on which they are stacked for quick use. Bands are marked with a serial number and the U.S. Fish and Wildlife Service address to which the band should be mailed.

Fancy Dress for Science

An eye-catching method of tracking birds is the gaudy device of dyeing them with bright colors. First used systematically by the California Fish and Game Department to follow the northward flight of geese, this technique immediately proved its value in bringing quick results as incredulous observers phoned in tales of pink, green and yellow geese all the way up to the Arctic Ocean.

As spectacular as the dyeing method is, it has its limitations. Because all birds molt, the dyed feathers are bound to be shed within a season. Nonetheless, the information to be gained from it can be useful in determining the behavior of local populations. In Boston, for example, dyeing was employed to check the movements of the clouds of gulls around nearby Logan International Airport, where they were a constant menace to aircraft. The study revealed that the birds were attracted by adjacent garbage dumps and by fishing fleets; control these and the airport menace might be reduced.

FRESHLY SPRAYED, a bright-hued gull lands among its pristine fellows. Although they look bizarre to humans, other gulls apparently see nothing odd in the dyed birds.

A RELUCTANT VICTIM, this herring gull is squirted with a scarlet spray in a project to ascertain the habits and range of gulls from six colonies along the New England coast.

A RUFFED GROUSE beats its wings in a throbbing courtship display to produce the resonant drumming by which it stakes its claim. Like a woodpecker's tapping, this is an example of nonvocal "bird song."

6

How Birds Communicate

Most birds seem to seek others' company. There are some exceptions, of course—loners such as the birds of prey, herons (when they are not nesting), grouse, rails, cuckoos, nightjars, kingfishers, dippers and some of the birds of tropical forests. But the large majority of bird species are social all the time. Doing things together requires a language, a means of communication. Birds have a variety of ways of sending messages—by voice, as well as by actions that may involve display of plumage or adornment: all devices and symbols by which they talk to each other.

The most obvious bird talk is song. Olin Sewall Pettingill, former director of the Laboratory of Ornithology at Cornell University, defined bird song as "a series of sounds consistently repeated according to some specific pattern and produced, as a rule, mainly by males and usually during the breeding season." This definition distinguishes song from call notes and other unrelated sounds birds make. Furthermore, by avoiding the word vocal, the definition includes the rhythmic tapping of woodpeckers, the wing-drumming of grouse and the aerial performances of woodcock and snipe, during which sounds are produced by means of notched feathers of the wings and tails.

BIRD-SONG NOTATION

Below are three different ways of transcribing the song of a bird—in this case, the eastern meadowlark. The first one, ordinary musical notation, can give only a rough approximation because birds do not restrict their musical vocabularies to our customary notes, intervals and tempos. The second, a musical shorthand system devised by Aretas A. Saunders, still depends upon the human ear, with its limitation in perceiving extra-high notes, tiny pauses, and very rapid trills. It required the development of the tape recorder and the oscillograph to make possible a scientifically accurate system of notation. Together, the two devices can produce a permanent record (bottom), called an audiospectrogram, which will show pitch (in kilocycles per second), volume (by thickness of line) and tempo.

Although they differ in detail and in technique, all three notations have the same general form: a pair of descending phrases of almost equal length, with the first pitched slightly higher than the second.

Some bird songs are so elaborate as to fall on the ears like phrases of divine music. The thrushes as a family are perhaps the most gifted of all singers. The male brown thrasher is another accomplished performer, and his repertoire includes more than 2,000 songs. Less-talented fowl often have voices that are discordant, insect-like or staccato. But whether the sound is monotonous or mellifluous, the vast majority of songs serve two functions: first, to proclaim the male's territory and warn other males away, and secondly, to advertise his maleness to an available mate and sexually arouse her.

Some people find it hard to believe that the "romantic" singing of the birds is often an announcement of status—tough talk to rivals. Singing becomes more frequent, more aggressive, when another male is within hearing. Should the interloper cross the invisible line that defines the territory, he is attacked, but usually a song is enough to send him on his way.

Even a badly stuffed male specimen planted within the domain of a singing male will be attacked, particularly if attention is drawn to it with a sound recording. But a robin will not attack a stuffed sparrow, wren or blackbird. It reacts only to other robins. David Lack of the Edward Grey Institute at Oxford, experimenting with England's little robin redbreast, discovered that the thing that made the bird "see red" was the red breast of its opponent. The robin would even violently attack a tuft of red breast feathers mounted on a wire. When the feathered wire was removed the bird still attacked the space where it had been. In North America the red "epaulets" of a singing red-winged blackbird are puffed out when it threatens a rival. Similarly, in Europe, the white shoulder patches of the familiar chaffinch are its battle banners. Bold patterns, colors and other bodily adornment act as "releasers," evoking the fighting response in other males while sowing the seeds of submission in females that are ready to mate.

Since a stuffed male will trigger an attack it is hardly surprising that a stuffed female will often elicit an equally appropriate reaction. A male may return to a stuffed female of the same species again and again to try to copulate. Brewer's blackbirds (even ones with mates) will actually approach headless and wingless specimens of the opposite sex. William Vogt, testing the emotions of a male yellowthroat, changed the apparent sex of a stuffed female by pasting a black mask across its face (the male yellowthroat has this mask, the female lacks it). When the male came back, its first reaction, according to Vogt, seemed to be one of shocked surprise, "as though its mistress had betrayed it"; then it attacked the deceiver.

As Niko Tinbergen, the Nobel Prize-winning behaviorist, points out, threat is in many species the first phase of courtship. When a female is attracted to a male by his song he may intimidate her at first. But she may disarm him by some sign of appeasement, some subtle gesture such as turning the head away (which is the standard procedure of the blackheaded gull), or she may express submission by acting like a baby, quivering her wings and begging to be fed. Courtship feeding is common in many songbirds and usually leads to mating. Song has a part to play here too. The songs of many male birds stimulate females to build nests. The completed nest in turn encourages them to lay eggs.

Singing is most persistent early in the morning and may taper off by midday. Thrushes sing most eloquently just before dusk. Perhaps the most tireless of all birds in the deciduous woodlands of eastern North America is the red-eyed vireo, which has been called the preacher bird because of the monotonous repetition of its phrases. The indefatigable Louise de Kiriline Lawrence reports that one male red-eyed vireo repeated this refrain 22,197 times between dawn and dark, a record not likely to be challenged except by another red-eyed vireo.

Birds that do not look alike may sometimes have rather similar songs—a junco and a pine warbler, for example. But it is axiomatic that birds of very similar appearance invariably have distinctive songs. There are many small flycatchers in the Americas, leaf warblers in Europe and birds of the nightjar-whippoorwill tribe throughout the world that look so much alike that they confound the experts until they speak. Song is the isolating mechanism that prevents these birds from making mistakes in choosing partners.

Song is also of the utmost importance to birds living in areas with dense vegetation. Often these birds are so inconspicuous in their surroundings that they must sing to attract attention. Reed warblers, inhabitants of the thick forests of Europe, sing far more often than sedge warblers, which can rely more on visual communication in their relatively open habitat.

It seems to be a rule of thumb that modestly colored birds are among the most gifted singers. There is perhaps a good reason for this: Whereas brightly colored birds tend to use their gay patterns to advertise themselves, many drab birds can advertise only vocally. Lacking bright feathers and quite lost in a big landscape, they climb into the sky to pour out their song. The skylark, colorless on the ground, dominates many acres of meadow from its aerial vantage point, showering down a tireless torrent of music.

How do birds learn to sing? In much the same way a human learns to talk. To begin with, one part of the bird's brain takes dominant control over language development—a situation paralleled in the human brain. Moreover, birds are genetically predisposed to learn to sing just as humans are genetically equipped to talk. In order to develop normal vocal patterns, birds, like humans, must be able to hear and mimic adults. At first, a young bird spends time groping for the proper sounds, as an infant does during its babbling stage. But since a bird's ability to learn its language reaches a maximum when it is quite young—usually within its first year of life—young birds quickly develop a full-fledged vocabulary.

Occasionally some birds do learn the songs of other species. The starling often mimics the wood peewee, killdeer and meadowlark in New England. Mockingbirds in California specialize in imitations of local woodpeckers and even of tree frogs. But on the whole, birds that learn the songs of species other than their own are relatively rare. Even mynas, those renowned mimics of human speech, learn only other myna birds' calls when living in the wild. When a bird is learning its species songs, it adopts the particular version sung by its closest fellows. This version in many cases is different from the one that is sung by members of the same species living elsewhere. Different versions of a species repertoire are called dialects. Not all bird species have dialects, but in those species that do, individuals tend to settle and breed in the area in which they learned to speak. Consequently, a geographical patchwork of avian-dialect areas has developed.

The dialects of some species change only gradually over considerable distances, but other species, such as the white-crowned sparrow in California's coastal chapparel, have established very sharply defined boundaries.

WHAT'S IN A NAME

The whippoorwill, the bobwhite and numerous other birds get their names from the sounds people hear them making. What people hear birds saying, however, depends very much on what country they live in. An interesting example is the list below of the various interpretations of the call of the chiffchaff, taken from the different translations of a "Field Guide to the Birds of Britain and Europe."

ENGLISH: chiff, chaff, chiff, chiff, chaff
FINNISH: til, tal, til, til, tal
GERMAN: zilp, zalp, zilp, zilp, zalp
FRENCH: tyip, tsyep, tyip, tyip, tsyep
DUTCH: tjif, tjaf, tjif, tjif, tjaf
SWEDISH: tji, tju, tji, tji, tju
SPANISH: sib, sab, sib, sib, sab
ITALIAN: ciff, ciaff, ciff, ciff, ciaff
ICELANDIC: tsjiff, tsjaff, tsjiff, tsjiff, tsjaff
DANISH: tjif, tjaf, tjif, tjif, tjaf

Standing at the boundary, one can hear sparrows to the north singing one dialect, while sparrows to the south sing another. Such an abrupt dividing line may discourage the two groups from interbreeding. In fact, the white-crowned sparrows on one side of the dialect boundary may come to differ so substantially from their neighbors across the border that they eventually develop into a new subspecies.

In dialect areas or in other places where the songs of neighboring birds are almost identical, males may toss the same songs back and forth to each other. This countersinging may involve expressions of dominance and subordinance, with the dominant male leading the singing and the subordinate male following. Such singing duels may help a female single out the better male to father her young.

Another type of musical gymnastics occurs in the tropics, where the female of some species will occasionally burst into song, joining her mate in a duet. Since many of these birds live in dense vegetation, duetting is an important means by which a couple can keep in musical touch with each other. The synchrony of the performance may be so precise that, to an observer who is not standing between the male and the female, the song sounds as though it comes from a single bird.

Even though two duetting birds can sound like one, the songs any two birds sing are never exactly alike. Each bird has subtle peculiarities to its song, and it is this difference—scarcely discernible to the human ear—that helps birds to recognize mates and neighbors and detect strangers. An Adélie penguin in a crowded antarctic rookery can recognize its mate by voice even after they have been separated for months. Penguin chicks will respond to their parents' voices played back on a tape recorder.

Tape recorders have revolutionized the study of bird voice. These instruments make it possible not only to compare call notes and songs critically but also, by putting the tapes through an oscillograph or a spectrograph, to analyze them visually. In fact, the science of bio-acoustics has revealed more about the classification of bird voices, their meaning and their individual ontogeny, or development, than had been found out by all the observers in all the preceding centuries.

The various sounds that birds make have been grouped by Nicholas Collias of the University of California into five main categories: (1) flocking and group movements; (2) food; (3) predators and enemies; (4) parent-young relationships; and (5) sexual behavior and related aggression. Song, of course, falls predominantly into the last category.

Migrating birds often utter special contact notes. Some of the sounds heard in the night sky, especially certain notes of low intensity, are a puzzle even to the expert, who must conclude, since he hears them only at night, that their special function is to communicate when birds cannot see each other. However, some families of North American birds—the wood warblers, the sparrows and the thrushes—are vocal during their nocturnal passage, while others apparently are not. The vireos, tyrant flycatchers and tanagers, all of which travel at night, seem to be silent.

The familiar quail of eastern North America has—in addition to its well-enunciated *bob-white!*—a "covey call," a querulous *ka-loi-kee?*, which is answered by a similar *whoil-kee!* This adult cry that brings the scattered flock together may have arisen from the peeping "lost" signal of the baby chicks.

Many flocking birds have their special feeding notes, assembly signals and flight calls. On the stubble fields where they graze, Canada geese converse in low, grunting notes. Loud honking cries signal take-off and as the organized wedge moves toward the horizon, the flock continues its stirring chorus.

Every bird has a vocabulary dealing with its most urgent preoccupation—food. Familiar to every farmyard is the brooding hen's excited food call, which brings her scattered chicks on the double. A young robin, having finished off a worm or two brought by its parents, may not make a sound for a while, but when hunger begins to reassert itself the youngster starts to utter light peeps, which give way to a louder note and finally to a two-syllabled call. These notes, becoming more insistent, help the parents to locate the fledgling if it has left the nest. When they finally arrive with the next meal, the youngster gives a little breathless cry that can only be interpreted as anticipation. A herring gull, finding a small amount of food, wolfs it down in silence, but should there be more than it can manage alone it proclaims its good fortune to every other gull within hearing with a three-syllabled cry.

It is possible that more cooperation exists among feeding birds than is recognized. In northern parts of Europe and America, woodland birds—titmice, chickadees, woodpeckers, nuthatches, tree creepers, kinglets—often hunt in mixed groups. Similar mixed flocks roam the tropical forests. It is quite likely that the various species recognize each other's calls—the starting notes, stopping notes, assembly calls, food calls and warning cries—in much the same way that an English-speaking person might in time learn to recognize basic meanings in French, German or Spanish without being able really to speak the language.

Though birds may cooperate, more often they compete for food. At a crowded feeding board they may threaten each other by voice or posture. A chickadee or a grosbeak gapes aggressively with open bill, an irritated nuthatch spreads its wings and tail. Actual fights are rare.

Warning cries may distinguish whether the menace is a hawk in the air or a dog, a cat or a man on the ground. A hen, spotting a hawk, has a harsh scream that sends her chicks into hiding but when a dog or man approaches, the alarm is a cackle.

CHICKADEES, when momentarily alarmed, sound a sharp chattering note that sends all nearby birds to cover, but the discovery of a small owl will elicit a distinctive, persistent and complaining call. Joseph Grinnell in California noted that a flock of bush tits, harassed by a small hawk, united in a shrill, quavering chorus that lasted for as much as two minutes and made it quite impossible to isolate any one bird by sound.

The biologists Hubert and Mabel Frings and their collaborators, experimenting with tape recordings, found that they could attract a crowd of cawing crows within six minutes by loudly playing the rallying call that crows give when they see an owl. Herring gulls fled from garbage dumps when their alarm calls were played back and starlings abandoned their roosts for a time until they apparently sensed that the alarm was a false one.

Some birds are so similar in appearance—for example, male and female terns, with their identical black caps and red bills—that they must have some device by which to tell each other apart. The male tern makes himself known by presenting a small fish, as a man would offer a box of flowers or an engagement ring. The two birds then fly ceremoniously over the colony,

HAWK OR GOOSE?

HAWK

DUMMY

GOOSE

To test how birds react to shape and movement in avoiding danger from the skies, an ingenious experiment was conducted. A dummy silhouette was constructed, midway in shape between a predator hawk and a harmless goose. When the dummy was towed through the air in one direction, it apparently resembled a long-necked goose, and chicks on the ground ignored it. But when it was towed in the other direction, the chicks froze in terror. Some scientists contend that the chicks, which had never seen hawks before, were reacting instinctively to the shape of the enemy bird of prey. Others believe that the chicks cringed not because they recognized a predator's silhouette but only because they feared an unfamiliar shape.

passing the symbolic gift back and forth. The crucial test comes when the male, settled on his territory, presents the fish once more. If it is accepted properly and the other bird submits to his pecks, there is no doubt that she is a likely partner.

Herons also have the problem of selecting mates from a crowd of birds that look exactly alike. Each species therefore has a ceremonial display that is shared by no other heron. The male night heron, for instance, dances on the nest site, extending his neck forward while treading with his feet. Then he spreads his plumes, lowers his head almost to the level of his feet and utters a short *plup-buzz*. This bizarre performance attracts amenable females, but they at first are driven off, until finally a lucky spouse is allowed to enter the nest platform—provided her legs have turned bright pink, which is a sign of full readiness to mate.

While the male heron and the males of many other species have elaborate dance and plumage displays for wooing the female, the drab-colored bower birds of Australia and New Guinea occupy themselves with fancy construction projects that bring color and beauty into their courtship rituals. The bowers of some species look like grand avenues in the grass; others resemble huts as high as nine feet (2.7 m). One species paints the bower walls with wet, powdered charcoal or fruit pulp; another decorates with living orchids, while yet another uses fruits, flowers, fungi and odd objects the male collects on the forest floor. Human artifacts are the rage among the bower birds. Purloined car keys, coins, jewelry, hair ribbons and handkerchiefs have been found at bowers. One male covered the lawn in front of his bower with used shotgun cartridges: Apparently the red shells with bright brass butts added a new dimension to his tricks for attracting the ladies.

CEREMONIAL displays do not necessarily end with the courtship ritual. Among some birds reciprocal greeting ceremonies strengthen bonds between a male and female long after they have mated. European white storks are almost mute, but a castanet-like rattling of the bill, audible for half a mile (0.8 km), serves them for communication. When the bird on the nest spots its mate winging homeward, it rattles, flinging its head backward until it touches the back, then throwing it forward in a stiff bow. The arriving bird joins in the display and they clatter in unison, tossing their heads, bowing and pirouetting with cocked tails and half-spread wings. Like the storks, many other water birds continue to perform their reciprocal displays even after the family of growing young begins to demand their attention. Gannets stretch their necks and cross their beaks in a ceremonious reassertion of their loyalties to each other.

Bird display may be an aggressive act aimed primarily at rival males. Wild turkey gobblers on promenade pay more attention to each other than to the hens. Shoulder to shoulder the big toms strut, their erect tails fully fanned and their stiff wing-quills dragging the ground. In the fever pitch of their rivalry their naked heads turn bright blue and their wattles become gorged with blood; when one bird gobbles they all gobble simultaneously. When a hen is ready to mate she prostrates herself before the tom turkey of her choice and he then mates with her.

Arena behavior, in which the males parade and perform on a chosen piece of ground, is a highly specialized form of bird courtship, in which the successful males breed with a number of females and females may breed with one or several males. The female generally chooses the male, but it is unlikely that lasting ties are formed and the males assume no nesting responsibilities. A number of grouse and other fowl-like birds have arenas where the cocks gather, and a variety of tropical birds are also known to hold court in forest arenas: the peacock-like argus pheasant of Asia, the birds of paradise of New Guinea, the bright-orange cock of the rock of South American mountains, the tiny manakins of tropical America and some hummingbirds. Jackson's whydah, which lives in the East African grasslands, may have an arena with as many as 100 individual dancing territories, each with a ring of trampled grass encircling a central tuft, around which a male dances; the tuft perhaps represents a symbolic nest.

Clearly the arena system makes it possible for a very small percentage of the males to perpetuate the species. One of the most fantastic of the arena birds, for instance, is the sage grouse of western North America. A large arena may be as much as half a mile (0.8 km) long and 200 yards (183 m) wide with 400 cocks stationed 25 to 40 feet (7.6 to 12.2 m) apart. Studies by James Simon and John Scott in Wyoming revealed that the flock, displaying and fighting every morning during a period of weeks, gradually establishes a hierarchy, with the most vigorous cock, the one most ready to strut and fight, occupying the key position. The remarkable discovery was that this dominant bird, the "flockmaster," mates with practically all of the hens, which walk to his station unmolested through the ranks of the less-privileged males. One such sultan served 21 hens in a morning. The flockmaster's immediate neighbors also share the females, but the males beyond the sultan's inner circle rarely get a chance to mate. Cocks tend to return to the same arena each year and establish a territory near their previous site. Only when dominant males weaken, leave or die can the celibate "outsiders" reach the central territories, where mating occurs.

In Europe, black grouse similarly divide their dancing grounds into individual territories. They begin by jumping and hooting, an activity that is highly stimulating to all concerned. Then each male, puffed out and literally shaking, challenges his rival with a bubbling *roo-koo*. With tails widespread and red eye-combs swollen, they make short aggressive rushes at each other. Only after each male has efficiently defended his territory is he ready to court any passing female that chooses to walk into it.

In the remnants of natural prairie in North America, prairie chickens still gather each spring on their dancing grounds, where the males strut, inflate orange neck sacs, erect hornlike neck feathers (pinnae) and make hollow booming sounds. This species and a similar prairie grouse, the sharptail, undoubtedly inspired some of the dances of the Plains Indians. In their arena the sharptails pivot with rapidly stamping feet, heads down, tails up. When one bird shuffles they all shuffle, when one stops they all stop, in perfect synchronization. The same postures, even the same steps, can be detected in the traditional dances of the Crees.

The ruff, a belligerent Eurasian sandpiper, is unique in that no two males in breeding plumage are exactly alike. Each is adorned with a neck ruff (very suggestive of the frilly ruffs once worn by Dutch burghers), which may be black, white, buff or rufous-red, and may be plain or barred in endless combinations. The males gather in a small traditional arena to jump, flap their wings and spar; seldom do they actually tangle in real combat. When the

BEGGING BEHAVIOR IN HERRING GULLS

A baby herring gull, just out of the shell, does not immediately associate its parent's bill with feeding. Instinctively, it pecks at the bright red spot near the tip of this long, thin object and receives, in return, a bit of regurgitated fish. So strong is the urge to peck that even a cardboard model (above) will do, if it has a prominent spot. The behaviorist Niko Tinbergen tested the reactions of newly hatched gulls with a variety of dummies, some of them shown below. All worked except the one at bottom left, which had no colored spot and elicited almost no response from the chick. A pencil-thin red rod with white rings on the end for supercontrast proved to be as attractive as the parent's bill.

plain-looking female, the reeve, enters the arena, she seems quite indifferent, whereas the males often appear to go into shock, crouching motionless while she stands near, possibly making her choice.

Before they are old enough to learn to dance, strut, honk or sing, birds have other ways of communicating. When a bobwhite lays a nest of eggs, the last of the eggs may appear days after the first ones. Yet all the young hatch on the same day and within several hours of each other. Ornithologists have discovered that the chicks themselves synchronize their hatching—and that they do this by communicating with each other. When an unhatched chick begins to breathe, it makes a clicking sound. The sound is audible when the egg is held close to the ear and apparently is audible from one egg to another when the eggs are touching. The rhythmic clicking seems to cause the retarded embryos to develop more quickly and the advanced ones to slow down. The synchronous hatching is an important safety mechanism since it permits the mother to escort all the chicks at the same time out of the nest to seek cover from predators.

Chick embryos communicate not only with each other, but with their parents as well. This explains in part the phenomenon known as imprinting, popularized by the animal behaviorist Konrad Lorenz. Immediately after it hatches, a gosling or duckling becomes raptly attached to its mother. Lorenz found that if he presented himself to newborn graylag geese hatched in an incubator, they immediately identified him as "mother goose." They followed him wherever he went and even swam with him in the Danube, ignoring other geese. Imprinting has now been demonstrated for a number of other birds and attachments have even been recorded between a bird and inanimate objects such as a box or a bottle.

Behaviorists once believed such imprinting was innate, but studies indicate that the mother-offspring bond is developed while a chick is still inside its shell. Experiments have shown that unborn ducklings clap their bills and emit sounds in response to their mother's quacking. Similarly, the guillemot embryo twists and calls in its egg, prompting its parents to turn the shell and utter feeding or luring calls. It is not surprising that newly hatched ducklings and guillemots respond so readily to their parents' calls.

ONCE a chick enters the world, it must communicate in order to survive. Even such a basic act as getting fed requires a special set of signals, though these seem for the most part to be automatic. For example, when a robin returns to the nest with food, young mouths fly open. But a hand held above the nest releases the same response, even before the chicks' eyes are open. Equally mechanistic is the reaction of the parent who, looking down, sees a brightly colored gape, perhaps one with a pattern of spots like the throat of a tropical orchid. Down goes the worm. The parent does not try to remember which nestling was fed last; it reacts to the stimulus of the widest gape. This works well, for the chick with the widest gape is most likely the hungriest. Feeding signals among herring gulls are just as effective. The baby gull, by pecking at the red or black spot on its parent's bill, stimulates the parent to regurgitate its food and feed the baby.

All such pecking, singing, calling and displaying is part of the birds' language. Often misunderstood or sentimentalized, it remains a fascinating field of study, an area in which man is learning more and more not only about how birds communicate, but also about what they say, and why.

WITH BASIC ACTIONS ANY BIRD COULD UNDERSTAND, A SONG SPARROW SEEING ITS IMAGE IN A MIRROR ATTACKS THE FANCIED INTRUDER

Language in Action

Song is only one of many ways in which birds express their social instincts, react to their environments and communicate with one another. From the plain aggressiveness shown by this song sparrow to the elaborate rituals of courtship, they can call on a remarkable repertoire of behavior to express themselves in ways often obvious, but often obscure enough to baffle ornithologists.

The Struggle for Living Space

Poets to the contrary, a singing bird is not necessarily greeting the spring or expressing joy in life. Birds sing primarily for two highly functional reasons—to proclaim their territory to other males of their species, and to attract and stimulate a mate. The harmonious sounds have emphatic meanings to other birds. A song that warns other males to keep out also serves as a declaration to females ready to nest that here is a male of property, able to support a household.

Among different species, however, territories may overlap, and the farm above, seen from a bird's-eye view, shows how eight American robins (brown lines) and three orioles (green lines) have staked out their living space. Though only two species are shown, this landscape could support as many as 10 or 20 kinds of birds with differing food requirements in peaceful coexistence. The season is mid-May, and two male robins (*lower left*), having already brought off first broods, are skirmishing over territories for second broods. The northern oriole (*upper right*), an aggressive singer, has just about finished establishing its territory and is ready to set up housekeeping for the first time.

129

PRESENTING A TWIG, a great egret hands over to its mate the job of guarding their eggs. Male and female alternate at this task. The changing of the guard is always marked by a dance-like ritual, with wings outspread and feathers fluffed, culminating in the presentation of twigs by the bird going off duty. Most egret couples do work together on their nests, but here, with the nest completed, the contribution is purely ceremonial. The twig itself may very well have come from the nest of the vociferous pair of roseate spoonbills on the left, which share the egrets' breeding territory in the Florida Everglades. Such pilfering sometimes leads to fights, but more likely a guttural squawk is all the protest the comparatively timid spoonbills dare to make.

A Courtship Ballet

Many birds court their mates with pomp and fervor, but the western grebe of the North American marshlands provides a particularly elegant ceremonial display. As mating season nears, the bulrush beds where grebes nest become the scenery for an elaborate water ballet.

As the dance begins, the male suitor may offer a likely mate a fish or a bit of water weed. He may rhythmically dip his bill in the lake or preen with exaggerated finesse. If the female accepts his advances she will respond in kind—and as spring progresses the shallows become a stage for small *pas de deux*, as grebes advance toward each other and back away, offer each other tokens or silently rear up, breast to breast, from the water.

For human observers, the dramatic climax of the grebes' ballet is the "rush." Two grebes will suddenly pivot, stretch up to their full heights and zoom off side by side across the water's surface like a pair of demented penguins. After racing for perhaps a hundred feet (30 m) they dive below the surface. This routine is repeated throughout the grebes' courtship. But mating means the end of the dance, as both sexes turn to the graver matters of building a nest and incubating their eggs.

RHYTHMICALLY BENDING TO PREEN, a male grebe *(right)* gives the final performance of a standard courtship ritual. His mate, whom he won by gracefully executing many similar bobbing and preening maneuvers, watches him from their nest.

A WARY CONFRONTATION is common between grebes that have not yet taken each other's measure. Harsh calls and menacing beak movements build the tension, which usually explodes in a frenzied "rush" *(top right)*. A male and female aggressively facing each other may well become season mates; two males may rush, competing for a nearby female's favor.

FEET MADLY CHURNING, a male and female skim over the foam in the famous grebe rush. The wild race ends when one grebe bows to the other's superior endurance and suddenly dives deep into the water.

A NESTING TOKEN, marsh foliage is full of meaning for this courting female. Because the monogamous grebes build nests of these weeds, the male to whom she presents her beakful can easily get her message.

133

Defending Territorial Rights

The boundaries that define a male bird's territory may be invisible to the human eye, but they are the focus of the bird's existence. As soon as his territory is established the bird patrols it with ceaseless vigor, proclaiming his sovereignty with bursts of song, fierce postures and sometimes even bloody physical attacks.

A bird will tolerate trespassing birds of other species on his territory, but an intruder of his own species provokes aggressive display. Even an intruder that is physically more powerful than the landlord seldom lingers long on the alien turf. Respect for the rights of the property owner is a notable characteristic. In the long run this instinct provides an effective biological mechanism for reducing competition among members of the same species, all of which need to have the same kind of food resources and nest sites for their survival.

SHIMMERING TAILS RAISED for aggressive emphasis, two superb male lyrebirds parry over a territorial boundary. The lyrebird marks out his territory by building low earthen mounds, like this one, along its edge.

FEROCIOUSLY GAPING, two male puffins each claim a rock on their nesting beach. A male usually declares his territory by showing his yellow mouth in a threat yawn. If an intruder draws near and opens his own beak, a fight may ensue.

A DUET OF HARSH CALLS warns trespassers away from the nesting area of this pair of sarus cranes. Their proclamation of territory is so effective that only rarely is the male *(right)* obliged to deal with an intruder through physical combat.

GAUDY GAPES like the red-yellow-and-white mouths of these yellow-hammer nestlings present obvious targets to parents delivering food. Bright mouth coloring is common among birds that are born helpless.

7

From Egg to Adult

ALL life must replace itself. In much of the world the annual cycle of the birds, which culminates in their reproduction, has its first vague beginnings when winter gives way to early spring. The foraging flocks are no longer as cooperative in their endless search for food. There is more bickering, more irritable chasing; fragments of song are heard for the first time. The increasing length of the day is affecting the birds' internal rhythm. Great changes are taking place in the gonads, the reproductive glands, which are under the control of certain hormones secreted by the anterior pituitary gland. The testes of a male bird may increase in size as much as several hundred times between its quiescent winter period and the peak of the breeding season that follows.

When nesting time approaches, just how does a bird select its territory? After considerable prospecting the male tends to return again and again to the same bush top or the same branch to sing his challenge. He may start with a plot of three or four acres (1.2 to 1.6 ha) with many favorite singing posts, but before he has settled his claim this may be whittled down to half that by neighboring males pressuring him. As James Fisher described it: "He plays them at song-tennis over the neutral ground between—ground that rapidly becomes less and less neutral. When one of these neighbors, now become a rival, alights in his area he makes a display flight at it, often singing on the wing; the neighbor retreats into his own area, and if he is followed, the roles are reversed; in such a way the boundaries of the territories are marked out." Years ago Frank Chapman determined the territorial boundaries of birds in his garden by putting up mirrors and noting where the males fought their images.

A singing male is nearly always invincible in his own domain. David Lack once confined a European robin in a cage within its own territory. When a neighboring robin trespassed, the bird in the cage put the intruder to flight simply by the vigor of its song. Conversely, when the caged bird was taken into the territory of its neighbor it cowered in terror, as it was prevented by the wire bars from flying away. In a similar experiment Arthur Allen of Cornell University placed a caged song sparrow within the territory of a rival. The confined bird went wild with fear and when the bird outside grabbed its wing tip through the bars, the caged bird had a heart attack and expired on the floor of the cage.

TERRITORY, as we have seen in Chapters 4 and 6, may be simply defined as any area that a bird defends against others of its own kind. However, perhaps the most functional aspect of territory is that it spaces birds out fairly evenly so that they all may be assured of enough food for their growing broods. Typical territories of songbirds in America may range from a half acre (0.2 ha) or less for some native robins, all the way up to 22 acres (8.9 ha) for meadowlarks. James Tanner in his study of the nearly extinct ivory-billed woodpecker in the southeastern United States found that a single pair, because of their very specialized habits, required a territory of not less than six square miles (15.5 km^2) of virgin swamp timber, whereas the same area could support 36 pairs of pileated woodpeckers or 126 pairs of red-bellied woodpeckers. A golden eagle, at the apex of the avian pyramid, may dominate a territory of more than 35 square miles (91 km^2).

Colonial birds are usually those with a mobile food supply—gleaners of the air such as swallows or swifts that may travel great distances in search of concentrations of flying insects, or sea birds whose luck depends on the vagaries of ocean currents and the schooling of fishes. The critical factor in the affairs of sea birds is a nesting place safe from four-footed predators, preferably an island, and when they find one it becomes the common property of all. They will cooperate in the defense of this communal breeding ground, and birds in a large colony have better nesting success than those in a small one. Within a colony each territory, if it can be called such, is reduced, in effect, to the nest site itself: the distance a bird can strike with its beak while sitting on its eggs. On Isla Raza in the Gulf of California more than 40,000 elegant terns often nest on a single acre of volcanic soil; that is one bird for every square foot (0.1 m^2). In some areas eggs are scarcely nine inches (23 cm) apart and the birds frequently lock their rapier-like bills with their neighbors while they brood.

In the northern United States, the first robin of spring and the last one to appear may be two months apart. The arrival of red-winged blackbirds may span three months. First to arrive are the stray birds, the vagrants, soon to be followed by high-plumaged males which claim territories they may have held the year before; then by the females; and lastly by the young males, which will fit into the population mosaic as vacancies permit. If a territory is vacant, it is quickly filled by such an unemployed male. We have already cited the replacement of birds in a Maine spruce forest after the resident birds were shot off. In a similarly ruthless but enlightening experiment in New Jersey some years ago, a male indigo bunting was collected after it had mated. By next morning the female had another mate. Nine times in about as many days the males were removed and each time the female quickly acquired another partner.

The female, on first arriving in a territory, is threatened by the male, just as the same male would threaten another male. But there is a difference; she neither fights nor does she fly away. By various subtle means she takes the aggressive wind out of the male's sails and his attitude switches to appeasement. She may not be fully conscious of the territory at first. She may wander away, only to be lured back by the irresistible song. There are sexual pursuits; the male desires copulation but she may not be ready. Or there may be special displays and perhaps courtship feeding. At any rate, the preliminaries are very stimulating and within a matter of days the female reaches sexual readiness; she is in harmony with the male and is receptive to copulation.

One or both of this pair, now on the threshold of mating, may have hatched from an egg only the year before. Most songbirds and ducks mate for the first time when they are scarcely 12 months old. Herring gulls, however, take at least three years to reach full maturity while eagles may take four or five. Sea birds like albatrosses, as noted, take longest of all: They do not mate before they are skilled enough at their trade to assume the responsibility of raising a chick.

The creation of the nest is inextricably tied in with courtship and sexual fulfillment. There is nothing in the fossil record to suggest how such a complicated habit evolved, but some ethologists believe it may have started quite simply—perhaps from the movements of the birds during sexual excitement. A female tern, for example, pivots on her breast to face the male who is circling about her with drooping wings, and eventually a saucer-like "scrape" is formed in the sand. Some terns lay their eggs in this depression without further embellishment; others add pebbles or sticks. The more complex nests of many other birds may have had just such simple origins.

Most nest building is done the natural way, while sitting. At first the bird may squat in a clump of grass, punching or molding it with its breast, or it may try to fit its body into a likely crotch in a shrub or tree. A few twigs or straws may be pushed into place. If they do not stick the bird may try another site. Eventually, by tucking, poking, pushing and molding, the cup takes shape.

No two species build identical nests. An expert observer does not always have to see the eggs to know the maker of the nest; the materials, size, structure and location are clues to his practiced eye. Nests vary from none at all, not even a scrape, as in the case of nightjars and other whippoorwill-like birds, which lay their well-camouflaged eggs on the bare ground, to the exquisitely woven purses of orioles and troupials and the complicated basketry of the weavers.

Just which birds make the smallest nests and which the largest is a matter of dispute. Some hummingbirds build nests scarcely an inch (2.5 cm) in diameter, but just as small is the tiny saucer of bark, down and dried glue in which the crested tree swift fits its single egg. A famous bald eagle nest at Vermilion, Ohio, measured eight and a half feet (2.6 m) in diameter, 12 feet (3.7 m) in depth and weighed about two tons (1.8 t). Another supernest built by a pair of eagles near St. Petersburg, Florida, had a diameter of nine and a half feet (2.9 m) and

A KNOTTY PROBLEM IN NEST CONSTRUCTION

Many of the sparrowlike weaverbirds of Africa are among the world's best nest builders. Their technique is based on the ability to hold down a grass strand with the foot (above) while wrapping, knotting or weaving the other end with the beak. The nest starts with the suspension of a woven ring of grass from a branch or leaf. The bird then stands in this ring and works in other long strands of grass all around until it is enclosed in a loose hollow ball slightly larger than itself. As many as 300 grass strands have been used in a nest. An inner partition keeps eggs from falling from the entrance at the bottom.

a depth of 20 (6.1 m). Even larger than these are the huge mounds of the megapodes, strange Australasian fowl that do not use their body heat to incubate eggs. Instead, they pile up heaps of debris which serve as incubators; the warmth of the fermenting compost does the work. In one species, the scrub fowl, a mound 20 feet (6.1 m) high and 50 feet (15 m) wide has been reported.

The tiny cobwebs-and-floss cup of the hummer and the gross untidy heap of the megapode are but two extremes in an extraordinary variety of avian architecture. Woodpeckers excavate their nurseries. These chambers, which often double as off-season sleeping quarters, are not lined; the eggs are laid on a bed of scattered chips. But the birds that make use of these holes when they are abandoned—titmice, wrens, flycatchers, swallows, bluebirds and others—build substantial nests inside.

The open-topped bowl typical of many land birds may be deep and felted like that of a goldfinch, shallow and twiggy like a dove's, or firmly woven of grass and hair as is a warbler's wont. The American robin and European song thrush reinforce their nests with a mortar of mud, and vireos and the chaffinch bind theirs together with cobwebs. Nests may be anywhere from the ground to 100 feet (30 m) or more up in the tallest trees, although only a small percentage are higher than 20 feet (6.1 m) and the majority are within six or eight feet (1.8 to 2.4 m) of the ground. The nests of most small birds are built in a week or less. A song sparrow in a hurry might finish a nest, and a good one too, in as little as three days, or it may dawdle along for nearly two weeks; its pace possibly reflects the stage of its glandular cycle.

Male wrens, overflowing with energy, build dummy nests or cock nests. In a reed bed where many globular nests of long-billed marsh wrens are fastened to the cattails, only one in half a dozen may hold eggs or young.

The mythical halcyon, the kingfisher, was rumored to lay its eggs on the quiet waters of the sea, hence the lovely term "halcyon days." Actually, kingfishers nest in tunnels they dig in riverbanks—or occasionally in the mounds of termites. Their nest burrows may extend for six or seven feet (1.8 to 2.1 m) but those of bee-eaters and some other earth excavators may be even longer.

No birds, of course, lay their eggs in the water, but grebes come close to it, laying theirs on small rafts of debris or decaying vegetation drifting about in the marsh. When the bird slips into the water it deftly pulls some of the vegetation over the eggs. This instinctive action serves two purposes: The eggs are concealed and, as a thermometer would reveal, their temperature is regulated. Ducks accomplish the same thing by wrapping their eggs in a quilt of down from their own breasts.

Mud is a useful medium for constructing nests. Flamingos make conical mounds which may be nearly two feet (0.6 m) high, building them up pellet by pellet. Cliff swallows and house martins fasten their mud jugs under ledges, bridges and eaves. The rufous ovenbird, the national bird of Argentina, mixes a mortar of sand and cow dung to construct a nine-pound (4.1-kg) ball with a door and an inner spiral threshold. The crossbar of nearly every telephone pole along the roadside supports one of these rock-hard ovens of *el hornero*, "the baker."

Among the most skilled bird artisans are those that suspend their nests. The vireos of North America weave firm little baskets hung from the V-forks of lateral twigs. The nests of orioles, swinging from the tip-ends of slender branches, are deeper and more purselike. Their colonial relatives, the oropendolas of the American tropics, knit "socks" three feet (0.9 m) long, taking a month to do it.

Twenty or 30 such bags may dangle from the perimeter of a single ceiba tree. The ultimate in simplicity of suspension is achieved by the green broadbill of Malaya, which hangs its intricately woven nest over a woodland pool by means of a single long woven string.

In building such hanging nests, the attachment of the first few strands of plant fiber presents a problem in engineering. The Australian rock warbler solves this by gluing its frail pouch to the roof of a cave by means of sticky spider webs. The weaverbirds of Africa and southern Asia actually tie knots. Some weavers build very sophisticated hanging nests which are entered through a sleeve projecting several centimeters below the globular nesting chamber, which itself has a little guard rail to prevent the eggs from falling through. Whether ingenuity or accident originally played a part in these designs we cannot know, but it is axiomatic that whenever a device favored survival it was likely to be preserved. Certainly in the tropics, where agile monkeys are a menace, the hanging nest is one answer to survival—and so is the frequent habit of building close to the nests of hornets and other stinging or biting insects, or even right inside, as some birds do, particularly in the nests of termites.

Few birds in the world construct weirder nests than the swifts. Most of the nearly 90 species of swifts employ their saliva, which hardens to the consistency of rock. The chimney swift of North America, which used to build in hollow trees, now glues its bracket of sticks on the inner wall of man-made stacks. The swallow-tailed swifts of tropical America use saliva and feathers to build feltlike tubes two feet (0.6 m) long that hang beneath rocky shelves. But the most improbable device of all is that of the palm swift of the Old World tropics, which glues its two eggs *upright* on a feltlike pad stuck onto a drooping palm leaf. Even when the leaf sways, flaps or turns upside down, the eggs stick, and so does the brooding bird.

The little cave swiftlets of the Indo-Australasian region use more saliva than other swifts and two kinds build their little bracketlike saucers entirely of this agglutinate material. These are the famous birds' nests of Oriental commerce from which such delicious soup is made. Tremendous numbers of swiftlets colonize some of the limestone caverns along the coast of Indochina, and here men reap their odd harvest with long poles, knocking down fresh nests which have taken more than a month to build.

The emperor penguin, the largest of the penguin family, needs no nest at all. Its single youngster is brought forth in the dead of the antarctic winter when the temperatures drop to 40° F. below zero (−40° C.). The female lays her egg in May just as the long antarctic night is setting in and the male immediately takes over. He places the egg on top of his feet, where the warm skin and feathers of the belly sag to form a protective mantle. Bracing himself against the coldest winds on earth, which may reach 100 miles an hour (161 km/h), and gaining some warmth from his fellows who crowd cheek to jowl on the ice, this breeding father patiently nurtures the germ of life for more than two months until the chick hatches. He will have lost 25 pounds (11.3 kg), a third of his weight, before the well-fed female slides in at last to relieve him and feed the chick.

Colonies such as those of herons or terns, which are like crowded cities with their individual homes, are not the only examples of how birds nest cooperatively. The emperor penguins in their milling pod on the ice are plainly cooperating. The sociable weaver of South Africa builds a regular apartment house so large that at a distance it might be mistaken for a native hut. As many as 100 pairs

AN OVEN OF CLAY FOR THE 'BAKER'S' EGGS

The rufous ovenbird of South America, nicknamed the "baker," builds a hollow ball for a nest from a mortar of sand and cow dung so strong that a thrown rock will not crack it. The nest above is cut open to reveal how the eggs are safeguarded by a semipartition between the entrance vestibule (right) and the nest chamber (left).

or more may build what appears to be a haystack 12 or 15 feet (3.7 or 4.6 m) in diameter in the branches of an isolated tree on the veldt. First to be built is the roof, and under it each bird tucks its own nesting chamber. In Argentina the monk parakeet builds similar collective dwellings of sticks with as many as a score of screeching families occupying flats in the main building.

Must birds learn how to build nests or do they know by instinct? We do not know to what extent the young bird's memory of its natal environs is important, but there is one case on record in which four generations of captive weaverbirds had no chance to build nests—but the fifth generation built them quite competently when they were given nest-building materials.

The laying of the eggs is synchronized with the building of the nest and may start the day after the last stick or straw has been pushed into place. Some birds take a breather for several days before beginning to lay. In most of the perching birds the usual rate is one egg a day, laid in the early morning, but the parasitic European cuckoo steals a march on its neighbors by sneaking in during the afternoon, to lay its own egg in another bird's nest. We tend to think of this as low cunning on the cuckoo's part, but more likely it is a result of natural selection: Cuckoos have profited by deviating from the morning routine.

Not all birds lay on a 24-hour schedule. Many have a somewhat longer interval; quite a few hawks, owls and gulls, for instance, lay on alternate days. Some eagles and condors space their eggs five days apart, while the mallee fowl has an interval of five to nine days (exceptionally, 16) and may take as long as four months to complete its quota. It can afford to take its time, since it is one of the megapodes, or mound birds, and is therefore not saddled with the tedium of incubation.

The number of eggs a bird lays might be taken as an index to its life expectancy. By inference, hummingbirds, laying only two eggs, have fewer hazards or greater longevity than wrens, which rear two broods of six or seven in a single summer. An albatross or a petrel lays but a single egg and if it is lost will not lay another that year. On the other hand, a pheasant or a duck may lay 12 or even 15 in a single clutch. These game birds have always led a precarious existence and it must not be concluded that their large broods are a direct result of gunning pressure—man is only one of many animals which prey on them and their eggs. But given half a chance they recover quickly from disaster; their reproductive potential is high.

The tiniest eggs are those of hummingbirds, pea-sized, almost always two and always white. Among living birds the largest, as one would expect, are laid by the ostrich. Five to seven inches long (13-18 cm) and with very thick shells, they take 40 minutes to hard-boil.

Tiny birds with prolific tendencies, such as blue tits, long-tailed tits, goldcrests and kinglets, may produce a single clutch that exceeds their own body weight. So may some ducks. A ruddy duck, which lays the largest eggs of any duck for its size, may weigh scarcely more than a pound (0.45 kg), whereas its average clutch of nine eggs tips the scales at nearly two pounds (0.9 kg) and a very large clutch of 14 or 15 would exceed three pounds (1.4 kg).

Not all eggs are "egg-shaped." The eggs of owls and toucans are nearly spherical. Those of the murres and other auks are pear-shaped, a decided advantage on the narrow rock shelves where they are laid, for they pivot without rolling off. The other seafowl that share the cliffs that jut out of the ocean—the gulls, cormorants and gannets—must build nests to keep their eggs in place.

Archaeopteryx and all the other dawn birds must have laid unmarked whitish eggs as reptiles do today. Many birds still lay immaculate white eggs, particularly those that nest in dark holes, where camouflage would be superfluous—the kingfishers, woodpeckers, swifts, parrots, owls, bee-eaters and practically all of the tropical hole nesters.

Most eggs laid in open nests are speckled, spotted, blotched or lined; some are very effectively camouflaged. Since the pigment that effects the coloration is deposited on the shell during its passage through the oviduct, much variation results and no two eggs are marked precisely alike. The pigment on the heavily blotched egg of a ptarmigan, almost blood-red when freshly laid, soon oxidizes until it becomes almost black. It has been suggested that these pigments, which are related to those of the blood and the bile, are merely by-products with no more usefulness or significance than the colors that appear on autumn leaves. True or not, what beautiful by-products!

Do birds recognize their own eggs? That is debatable. In a colony of terns the egg patterns vary from tiny specks to large blotches and, nesting as they do often only a beak's thrust from each other, it would seem that egg recognition would be important to terns. However, experiments show that even in such crowded circumstances it is the site that is the magnet. A tern will brood even a flash bulb if it is in the right place. If its own egg (or any egg) is placed several inches in front of the empty nest it will retrieve it, rolling it back into the scrape, but at a greater distance the same egg will be ignored. However, on Midway Islands, when a sooty tern (which lays only one egg) was given a choice of two eggs, it usually retrieved its own, so apparently there is recognition.

Other colonial birds react in much the same way. A herring gull will brood brightly painted wooden eggs and night herons will accept wooden blocks with sharp corners though they can see their own eggs two or three feet (0.6 to 0.9 m) away.

Songbirds, even those that nest on the ground, will not retrieve their eggs should they roll outside the rim. Some species will also refuse to brood the eggs of cowbirds, seeming to recognize that they are unlike the rest. Most small birds, however, readily accept the eggs of these parasites; they may even be stimulated by their large size.

Nearly 80 species of birds belonging to several families are completely parasitic at nesting time, laying their eggs in nests not their own and leaving the care of their young to their hosts. A number of other species are partially parasitic, usually building their own nests and caring for their own young but sometimes laying in other nests. The greatest number of these "nonobligate" parasites are found among the ducks. More than 20 species lay, at least occasionally, in the nests of their neighbors, and one, the redhead of North America, does so more often than not. Milton Weller records that 13 different female redheads laid eggs in the same nest and as many as 87 eggs have been found in a single "dump" nest. Only one duck, the black-headed duck of South America, is believed to be completely parasitic, for no nest has ever been recorded. Its eggs have been found not only in the reedy baskets of other ducks but also in the nests of gulls, glossy ibises and even chimangos, small birds of prey!

The honey guides, essentially African, parasitize their relatives, the barbets. To insure its survival the bill of the young honey guide at birth is equipped with a pair of hooks, as sharp as needles, with which it gives a fatal nip to its nestmates. A few days later, the hooks, which are no longer needed, simply fall off.

A PATERNAL THERMOSTAT

MALLEE FOWL

The mallee fowl uses the heat of fermenting vegetable matter to help incubate its eggs. They are deposited in a huge pile of decaying leaves and trash collected by the male bird and covered by a layer of sand. Proper temperature is maintained by constant adjustment of the sand covering. This task is practically the lifetime career of the mallee male (shown below testing the temperature with his beak). The female is permitted to approach the mound only to lay an egg, which she does about once a week for several months. As each chick hatches, it struggles unaided up through the sand to face life on its own. Neither parent seems to recognize its offspring.

MALLEE NEST

The most famous of all parasitic birds is the cuckoo of Eurasia and Africa. More than 300 species of birds are parasitized by this master nestfinder. To make room for itself in a small nest the young cuckoo squirms and shoves until its nestmates or the unhatched eggs are heaved overboard. The oölogists Edgar Chance and Stuart Baker assert that a cuckoo tends to lay its eggs in nests like the one in which it was raised and the eggs are surprisingly similar to those of their hosts, even as to color. Perhaps imprinted with the nest of its foster parent, the bird carries this impression through life. One strain of cuckoos may lay only in the nests of meadow pipits while another may specialize in willow warblers. Their critics say that Chance and Baker may be right, but they nevertheless argue that the two failed to color-mark the adult cuckoos to verify their identity.

Whereas half of the Old World cuckoos are parasitic, the New World cuckoos, with only four exceptions, are not. However, both the yellow-billed and the black-billed cuckoo of America will occasionally lay in other nests. It is among some of these occasional or partial parasites that we find hints about the intriguing question of how the parasitic habit evolved.

In the New World the cowbirds are the main parasitic group. Each young cowbird is raised at the expense of one or two young of its host, a fact that causes biologically unaware "bird lovers" to smash every cowbird's egg they find. Generally, the survival rates of cowbirds are no greater than those of their host species and removing the cowbird's eggs does not necessarily increase the numbers of redstarts, song sparrows or red-eyed vireos. This generalization, however, may not apply if the host population is already declining steadily; in 1972 and 1973, when cowbirds were removed from nests of the endangered Kirtland's warbler, the warbler population grew.

Some birds are "determinate" layers. A typical sandpiper or plover lays four eggs, and if one is taken it does not make up the loss; it always lays four, then stops. "Indeterminate" layers will keep on if their eggs are taken. They apparently must feel the right number in the nest before they stop. A flicker whose egg was removed daily laid 71 eggs in 73 days; a European wryneck laid 62 eggs in 62 days. Domestic fowl are in this category; the record for a chicken is 361 eggs in a year. A duck once laid 363 eggs in 365 days.

Broodiness is thus triggered in one of these two ways: by the physiological process of having laid the right number of eggs or by the tactile sensation of sitting on the right number. Most perching birds and precocial birds (ducks, geese, grouse, etc.) do not start incubation until the clutch is about complete. This gives all the young, which hatch fairly close together, an equal start in life.

**ALTRICIAL BIRDS—
HELPLESS AT BIRTH**

The young of most birds are blind, naked and utterly helpless at birth. They emerge from the egg in a relatively undeveloped condition and require constant parental care and feeding until they gain strength, grow feathers and are able to leave the nest. Birds of this type are called altricial. Reflecting the short time that they spend in the egg, their eggs tend to be small. The meadowlark, a typical altricial bird, hatches in about two weeks and leaves the nest 10 to 12 days later.

MEADOWLARK AND EGG

DAY-OLD CHICK

Hawks, owls, parrots, herons, storks and a number of other large birds, however, incubate from the day the first egg is laid, with the result that the youngsters hatch at intervals. There is often such a difference in sizes in barn owls that one owlet may kill and eat a younger when the latter hatches.

Although the embryo, the germ of life, begins to develop even before the egg leaves the warmth of the bird's body, its growth stops briefly when the egg is laid, to resume when the birds start the long—11 to 80 days—job of incubation. The embryo grows fast, absorbing the white and most of the yolk. A day or two before hatching it actually starts breathing, taking its oxygen from the air chamber and through the porous shell. Meanwhile the shell is getting weaker, for much of its calcium has been absorbed by the growing skeleton.

Merely sitting on the eggs does not ensure their incubation. Feathers are insulation; to transmit heat to the eggs birds develop "brood spots," bare patches on the underbody. The down falls out, the fat disappears and a concentration of blood vessels raises the temperature of the skin. Settling on the eggs, the bird parts its abdominal feathers and shimmies its body so that these spots come into comfortable contact with the eggs. In general these patches, numbering from one to three in different species, are present only in the sex that broods; if both sexes share the labor, both usually have them. But not all birds have this thermostatic incubation aid. Ducks do not, but they compensate by pulling out the down themselves and adding it to the nest. Gannets place a big webbed foot on the single egg, and this acts like a warming pad.

Perhaps as often as 12 times an hour, the bird turns the eggs or adjusts them to the brood patch. However, they need not be covered constantly. Although the average temperature of an egg may be in the low 90s F. (about 33° C.), it is addled more readily by exposure to sun than by cooling. Herons, terns, sandpipers and other birds that spell each other (often with an ostentatious change-over ceremony) may brood nearly 100 per cent of the time. But in most perching birds, where the female alone is responsible, she may spend 15 to 30 minutes at a time on the eggs and then take a break of anywhere from six to 10 minutes for feeding. Sometimes "helper" birds assist the parents. Helpers may be immature birds of an earlier brood, nonbreeding adults or even breeding adults of the same or a different species. The most common form of aid is in feeding the young, but nest building, incubation and brooding are among other helper activities. For example, among some jays, yearling helpers assist breeding birds by feeding the nestlings and guarding the nest.

Incubation may take as little as 11 days in some of the perching birds, but as long as 80 days in kiwis and large albatrosses. There is one record of a mallee

DAY-OLD CHICK

KILLDEER AND EGG

PRECOCIAL BIRDS— ACTIVE AT BIRTH

Certain birds, like the killdeer, are able to fend for themselves almost immediately on hatching. They are known as precocial. Although the killdeer is about the same size as the meadowlark, its egg is considerably larger, reflecting the longer time (24 to 28 days) its chick will remain inside before hatching and also the greater amount of yolk needed to feed this larger chick. Some precocial chicks can run and feed themselves in an hour; others are unable to do so for as much as two days.

fowl's egg that took 90 days' incubation to hatch (instead of the average 62).

The mallee fowl, incidentally, takes extraordinary care of its incubator nest. The male spends more than five hours a day regulating the temperature of the nest-mound, testing it with his beak or tongue. By opening up the mound or piling on more sand he keeps the egg chamber at an even 92° F. (33.3° C.). This mound is not a laborsaving device, for the male spends 11 months a year tending it. One relative, the maleo of Celebes, lays its eggs in the warm volcanic sands of beaches and even near hot springs or steaming volcanic fissures.

The family relationship of the mallee fowl is almost reptilian; the chick never knows either parent. As soon as it burrows out of the mound, which may take from 2 to 15 hours, it is on its own and fully able to fly. No female has ever been seen with a brood. The biographer of this strange bird, H. J. Frith, points out that if the female were to collect her year's progeny she would ultimately have a brood of up to 30 chicks, varying in age from a few days to several months.

To break, or "pip," the shell, the unborn bird is equipped with an "egg tooth," a small horny nubbin on the tip of the upper mandible with which it chips away at its prison. A sign of the bird's reptile ancestry, this temporary growth disappears soon after birth, just as it does on the snakes and lizards that also have it. The actual hatching process may take from several hours to a day or more. As much as two days before hatching, the chick may be heard peeping faintly within the shell and it is then, according to Tinbergen, that the parent first regards the fetus as a chick, not an egg.

When the struggling young bird finally kicks itself free, the parent may eat the empty shell or take it some distance away if the young are not the sort that leave the nest right away. Grouse, quail and ducks, whose chicks can walk when they are hatched, usually abandon the castoff shells where they are.

T HE young of birds fall into two main categories. Those that are helpless, born blind, naked and feeble, with little talent at first except to open their mouths for food and to defecate, are called *altricial*. The helpless young of some sea birds, herons, hawks and owls are also included under this term even though they may start life with a covering of down. *Precocial* chicks are fully clothed, bright-eyed and able to run after their parents and peck at things as soon as the down dries. The rule of thumb is that precocial birds lay larger eggs than altricial birds of similar size.

The precocial bird, born alert, has a relatively long infancy; the altricial bird, often eating its own weight in a day, soon outstrips it. A young songbird, born naked and helpless, eats and grows at a furious rate. A young European cuckoo, two grams at birth, weighs 50 times as much three weeks later. During this period of intensive bodybuilding, the diet of young birds runs heavily to insects, even though it may shift later to seeds or fruit.

If the young may be called growth machines, the parents are tireless feeding automatons. A pair of phoebes was reported to make 845 trips to the nest in a day, a pair of great tits, 900. An eagle, on the other hand, may make only two or three daily trips, but the prey it brings to its hungry young is large.

Whether the fledged bird is a warbler that leaves the nest in nine days and is fed for two weeks longer or an albatross that makes its first flight to sea at the age of six months, it is at last on its own and the next few months will prove whether it will survive. Mortality is greatest in the first year. When the next breeding season rolls around, there should, in theory, be just about the same number of pairs on territory as there were the year before.

TAKING ITS TURN FORAGING, A MALE RED-NECKED GREBE RETURNS TO THE FAMILY'S FLOATING HOME WITH A WATER INSECT FOR ITS YOUNG

The Family Life of Birds

Each spring, as the warmth and light of lengthening days wake the landscape, birds begin their annual cycle of courtship, reproduction, nest-building, incubation and brooding their young. Some birds carry out only a few of these functions in the course of brief liaisons. Others form close-knit, enduring families or even large communities. But either way, new life for the future is insured.

A MALE WANDERING ALBATROSS STARTS COURTSHIP BY FLAPPING ITS WINGS (LEFT). AFTER SOME NIBBLING, IT ATTRACTS ANOTHER FEMALE

The Ritual of Courtship

Birds, like people, when courting put their best foot forward, showing off their particular skills or attributes to the greatest possible advantage. Thus, versatile fliers like the skylark or the woodcock engage in impressive courtship flights, while species with highly spectacular markings, like pheasants and peacocks, resort to elaborate plumage display to attract prospective partners. Among many sparrows and other dull-coated species, however, the sexes look pretty much alike, so that these birds must rely on song rather than sight to find a mate. Still other birds have evolved long, intricate rites that strengthen the bond for the many months the pair will spend together caring for the eggs and young. Examples of birds with remarkable dances are the cranes, the whistling-ducks and the nibbling, hopping, yowling albatrosses prancing across these pages.

HUGE WING SPAN of a wandering albatross, like this one photographed on a subantarctic island, may be 11 feet (3.4 m).

148

SOON THE INTRUDER IS DRIVEN AWAY AND THE PAIR REACHES A CLIMAX (BELOW) AS BOTH BIRDS STRETCH THEIR WINGS AND SHRIEK LOUDLY

A NEWLY LAID EGG

5 DAYS OLD

15 DAYS OLD

23 DAYS OLD

Stages in the Development of the Avian Egg

Although the time it takes an egg to hatch varies considerably among species, the growth process inside the shell is the same for all birds and is illustrated in these photographs of a turkey embryo in different stages of its development. The newly laid egg shows little more than a huge yolk which will

12 DAYS OLD

29 DAYS OLD

nourish the growing chick. Five days later, the embryo's outlines are already visible and a network of blood vessels that absorb sustenance from the yolk has radiated across its surface. By the 12th day, except for a single connective stalk, the embryo is completely separated from the shrinking yolk. At 15 days various organs can be clearly discerned, particularly the eyes. At 23 days the bird is fully formed and begins to absorb the remaining yolk into its abdomen. Finally, about four weeks after the egg was laid, the living bird accepts its first challenge and beaks its way into the world outside.

A NEED TO BITE helps insure the survival of a baby African honey guide. Immediately upon hatching, it instinctively uses the sharp hooks on its bill to nip and kill the rightful occupants of the nest, most often young barbets. Their work done, the hooks drop off. Honey guides, like most parasites, are laid only one to a nest. If more were laid, they would begin killing each other off.

Deadly Nestmates

Not all birds are good homemakers. Some species, particularly the cowbirds and cuckoos, depend on others to do this work for them. The bay-winged cowbird, for example, often waits for another bird to build a nest, then appropriates it. But as soon as this is done, its cousin, the screaming cowbird, may sneak in and lay an egg in the bay-wing's stolen nest. The African widow bird, also a busy parasite, mates with a succession of females, each of which may then lay her eggs in different waxbill nests.

The interloper's egg is often the first to hatch. Being older and usually bigger than other nestlings, the parasite can get rid of them by pushing them about, stepping on them and starving them. The adult birds do not discriminate between the babies they feed; they simply stuff food into the biggest and nearest mouth. A few parasites eliminate nestmates directly, as is illustrated above and below.

AN IMPULSE TO SHOVE impels a blind European cuckoo— which hatches earlier than its nestmates—to work the eggs of a tree pipit out of the nest, leaving only itself to be raised by the foster parents. The pushing reflex, which lasts some four days, is set off when a sensitive area on the bird's back comes into contact with solid objects like eggs, chicks, and even marbles.

AN INSTINCT TO FEED whatever lies in its nest has impelled this dunnock (or "hedge sparrow") to go on dropping insects in a cuckoo's mouth after the latter has outgrown its host and left the nest. Hosts even perch on adopted chicks' backs to do the job. Pipits, warblers and other small parasitized birds will continue to cater to imposters several times their own size.

GREAT HORNED OWL
Bubo virginianus

NORTHERN ORIOLE
Icterus galbula

BLACK SKIMMER
Rhynchops niger

COMMON MURRE
Uria aalge

COMMON SNIPE
Gallinago gallinago

AMERICAN COOT
Fulica americana

SCRUB FOWL
Megapodius freycinet

SNOWY EGRET
Egretta thula

EMU
Dromaius novaehollandiae

NORTHERN CARDINAL
Cardinalis cardinalis

GUIRA CUCKOO
Guira guira

AMERICAN ROBIN
Turdus migratorius

BROWN KIWI
Apteryx australis

NORTHERN JACANA
Jacana spinosa

BROAD-BILLED HUMMINGBIRD
Cynanthus latirostris

ELEGANT CRESTED TINAMOU
Eudromia elegans

GLOSSY-MANTLED MANUCODE
(BIRD OF PARADISE)
Manucodia ater

AMERICAN CROW
Corvus brachyrhynchos

WHITE PELICAN
Pelecanus erythrorhynchos

The Diversity of Eggs

The largest bird egg known is that of the extinct elephant bird, shown here in white outline behind some representative eggs of living birds, all painted in actual size. This huge egg held over two gallons —30,000 times as much as the smallest hummingbird's egg; its shell was also 75 times as thick.

Generally speaking, egg size is related to that of the bird that lays it, but there are some notable exceptions. The kiwi, for example, is less than half the size of the white pelican, but its egg is several times as large. It is, in fact, the largest in proportion to its parent's size of any egg. This also explains its long shape; if it were rounder, the female could not lay it. Eggs laid on sea ledges, like the murre's, are often sharply tapered. If they roll, they roll in tight circles and do not fall off.

Differences in color seem to mean little, except that speckles camouflage eggs laid on the ground. White eggs often belong to birds that nest in holes or burrows—their conspicuousness is no problem.

155

HALF-BUILT HANG NEST of a male baya weaver will soon be completed now that the tiny tropical architect has lured a shopping female into sharing it. This type of nest provides excellent protection against marauding monkeys and tree snakes of the Asian jungles.

SEWN HOME of the redheaded tailorbird is actually stitched together with plant fibers. The bird punches holes along the edges of

A PRIMITIVE SCRAPE in coarse sand surrounded by a few pebbles and vegetation serves the arctic tern as a nest. The bird spends most of its life traveling and uses but little time to build.

A Diversity of Architecture

There are almost as many ways to build nests and as many materials from which to construct them as there are species to build them. Mud, wood chips, feathers, stones, twigs and grass are among the popular substances used to form homes that may be as crude as the vague depression made in the grass by the red-necked loon, or as elaborate as the snug, two-roomed sand and dung house of the rufous ovenbird. Saliva is often used by swifts to cement materials together. Many species are attracted by bright decorative objects like pins, papers, wires, golf balls and bottles, which they incorporate into nest construction. In fact, one observer reported that large green leaves with its bill and threads fibers through the holes, expertly drawing the leaves into a cup to hold its dangling nest.

GRASS HOUSE of the reed-dwelling yellow-eyed babbler is bound with silver-gray strands of spider cobwebs. These strong filaments also anchor the structure firmly between stems. The whole nest is built close to the ground and concealed by the foliage.

a pair of Bombay house crows formed a nest with some $70 worth of gold eyeglass frames, which they had taken from an open shopwindow.

Sometimes male and female will work together to build a home, alternately gathering material and shaping the nest. Such cooperation is notable among kingfishers, swallows and woodpeckers. Just as often, one or the other sex will take on the whole job. But whether the final product is simple, sloppy, neat or as intricate as the nests seen above, it usually provides at least two basic amenities: safety from predators and close proximity to a source of food, and often shelter against extreme weather.

FLIMSY STRUCTURE of the mourning dove is built both by the male, which gathers the material, and the female, which does the actual building. This one in a cactus is safe from predators.

EXTRACTING PIGEON'S MILK, a secretion chemically similar to rabbit's milk, a white-faced quail dove sucks at the inner side of its parent's crop. Both sexes manufacture the fluid.

Predigested Meals

The majority of perching birds feed their young by the familiar method of placing their insect-laden beaks directly in the hatchling's mouth. But some orders, particularly the big sea birds, have developed more complex feeding techniques. These birds swallow their food where they catch it, semidigest it and regurgitate the gruel back at the nest. This not only lets the bird carry more food per trip, but it also helps the youngster to digest it, since the parent regurgitates digestive juices along with the marine creatures it has swallowed.

The simplest form of this kind of feeding is found among gulls and storks. They throw up the food in front of the nestlings, which quickly devour it. Adult albatrosses and spoonbills go a step further; they grab hold of the hatchling's beak crosswise in their bills and shovel the food down with their tongues.

MINING A MEAL from within its parent's gullet, this brown pelican chick and its nestmate will each consume 150 pounds (68 kg) of regurgitated food before they are old enough to fly.

A JUICY MASS OF LARVAE is rammed into an avid chick's beak by a black-throated green warbler. This warbler is one of the many small species that make 200 or more food sorties each day to quell the fierce appetites of their dependents. The male warbler assumes much of the responsibility during the feeding period, making three times as many trips as the female.

A FECAL SAC is removed from its nest by a female lyrebird *(above)* and added to previously discarded sacs in a nearby stream *(below)*. These sacs of thin membrane, formed in the intestines of young birds, make neat packages for disposal of body wastes. They are important to the survival of low-nesting species, for without them the droppings might lure predators.

Parental Care

Along with providing food, many adult birds take extensive care of their young, brooding them, enticing them to fly and to gather their own food. The infant bird is born a damp, cold-blooded animal. A brooding parent immediately gathers the chick to its body to dry it out, encourage growth and protect it until it makes a remarkable transition and becomes a warm-blooded creature. This transformation may take as little as two to seven hours, as among common eider ducks, which live and breed on the cold, foggy northern coasts, or as long as 21 days, as among cliff swallows of the milder temperate zones.

Parent birds must also devise a variety of ways to defend their hatchlings. Some, like terns, will threaten or attack an enemy, screeching and swooping until, only inches away, they wheel and fly off. Grouse have evolved a more effective defense: They signal their young to freeze until danger passes. Grebes carry away their threatened young on their backs.

Ultimately, however, fledglings must leave the nest. The whistling-duck calls to its offspring from the ground; the pygmy nuthatch pulls them from the nest hole; the chachalaca carries them, clinging to its legs, from nest to earth.

COLLECTIVE CARE is practiced by emperor penguins after their young are big enough to gather in "kindergartens." Penguins are such avid brooders that they will fight to mother a stray.

INDIVIDUAL CARE characterizes the swan, seen here brooding its young. Although able to swim and feed themselves right after hatching, the young stay with adults some nine months.

WATTLES AGLOW in the sun, turkeys throng a Virginia corral where they are fattened by scientific care and feeding. Well over 100 million a year now are raised in the United States, more than 100 times the estimated population of wild turkeys.

8

Toward a Balance with Man

O F all the world's birds, none has had a more intimate association with man nor contributed more to his welfare than the red jungle fowl, *Gallus gallus*. From this one species of pheasant all the many varieties of domestic chickens have had their origin and today the number of individuals runs into the billions, making it by far the most numerous bird on earth—far more numerous, indeed, than the human race. Although originating in the jungles and bamboo thickets of southeastern Asia, it has penetrated to almost every corner of the world, wherever man has taken root, except in frigid climates. Of all man's satellites only dogs have become acclimated more widely.

We cannot quite be sure when humans first took these fowl into their compounds and domesticated them, but it was probably about 4,000 years ago. *Gallus gallus* seems to have reached central Europe as early as 1500 B.C. and was well established there by the time the Romans came. Long before the white man's ships explored the Pacific, the Polynesians had carried fowl to the Hawaiian Islands and wild variants of the original stock can still be seen in the rain forest on Kauai. In fact, there have been claims that the seagoing Polynesians brought the first chickens to the New World. Association

165

FOUR FOUNDERS OF ORNITHOLOGY

COMTE DE BUFFON

Georges Louis Leclerc de Buffon (1707-1788), despite an unscientific tendency to humanize birds and animals, helped to establish ornithology as a science through his 10-volume, color-illustrated "Natural History of Birds" and his personal prestige as a member of the French court.

ALEXANDER WILSON

The Scottish-born Wilson (1766-1813) did not live to complete his projected 10-volume work on American birds. The eight volumes he finished, however, which were published before the work of his rival, Audubon, earned him the title of "the father of American ornithology."

with man has meant a sort of welfare state—protection and assurance of food—but the birds pay for this relative security with their eggs and their meat. While their wild brethren in the forest have remained virtually unchanged, the domestic birds have developed a hundred standard breeds or more. Through selection and special feeding some have become very much larger with heavier layers of meat. Egg laying has been increased to the point where champions may lay an egg nearly every day in the year.

While the hens were developed as egg factories, the natural pugnacity of the cocks appealed to the competitive instincts of some people and fighting strains with powerful legs and longer spurs were bred. Such birds bear a closer resemblance to their wild ancestors than most other breeds. But as man became more civilized he began to experiment with ornamental varieties. Here was a bird that was particularly plastic and, as William Beebe aptly put it, "the aesthetic side of mankind seized upon this as a sort of living, organic potter's clay." Some of the products of the fanciers' ingenuity are truly beautiful, others are bizarre, and some can only be described as monstrous. Giants and midgets have been bred, birds with stiltlike legs and others with absurdly stubby legs. There are crested varieties, frizzled fowl with every feather turning outward from the body and rumpless breeds. One of the most extraordinary (and also most useless) products of the breeder's art is the famous long-tailed fowl of Japan, the *Onagadori*, which has been known to attain magnificent tail feathers that stretch to as much as, even more than, 20 feet (6.1 m) in length.

Although ornamental breeders vie with each other, the main objective of the thousands of poultry shows throughout the land is to improve the production of eggs or meat. In 1890 the 500-hen poultry farm was a source of wonder; today some farms boast one million or more. In most of these poultry factories the chicken run has been eliminated and the "battery method" is used. Living a completely synthetic life, the birds are raised entirely indoors in wire-bottom cages several shelves high, a far cry from the habitat of their jungle-bred ancestors.

In the United States poultry is now a multibillion-dollar industry. The laying flock is sustained at around 300 million while nearly three billion are raised yearly as broilers. Egg production is something like 64 billion per year, nearly one egg a day for every person in the United States.

Whereas the economic importance of chickens has to be measured in billions of dollars, that of the roughly 13 million domestic ducks marketed yearly in the United States amounts to only a few million. These are raised for their meat and most of them, even though they are sluggish, potbellied and white, are descended from the handsome, green-headed wild mallard. Wild ducks are far more important economically: Pursued by nearly two million American sportsmen—most of whom not only buy duck stamps each year, but also spend considerably more for equipment, travel and lodging—ducks support or help support a wide range of industries and services.

The turkey is America's great contribution to animal husbandry. The yearly hatch of poults often exceeds 100 million and it is almost certain that there are more turkeys in domestication today than ever roamed the primeval forest in pre-Columbian times. The Mexican race of the wild turkey had already been domesticated by the Indians when Mexico fell to Cortez. The returning conquistadors introduced the bird to Europe and by 1530 it was quite well established there, so when the Pilgrims celebrated their first Thanksgiving in

Massachusetts they undoubtedly were already familiar with the tasty fowl which the local Indians furnished for the feast.

It is a tossup whether chickens or pigeons are man's feathered associates of longest standing, but if we accept Biblical legend, Noah was the first pigeon fancier. Certainly the Egyptians raised pigeons for food and probably to carry messages as early as 3000 B.C., long before chickens reached the land of the Nile. Just when they were first used as a means of communication in war is not known, but Julius Caesar used them to send news of victory and they continued to play an important role as message bearers right down to World War II, when electronics finally largely supplanted their services.

Today pigeons are still raised by the millions throughout the world, as squabs to eat, for ornament and particularly for racing. More than 200 ornamental breeds are recognized. Pigeon racing, which has hundreds of thousands of devotees, was given a great impetus by the air age, which made it possible to transport birds hundreds of miles to their release points in a matter of hours.

THE progenitor of most, if not all, of the varieties of domestic pigeons is the rock dove, which still breeds wild on European sea cliffs. It is quite likely that wild birds first took to town life around the mosques and temples of southern Asia. Today most large cities have their self-sustaining flocks, for the high stone buildings are not unlike the ancestral sea cliffs.

Bird pets have probably graced the homes of men since the Bronze Age, but the cheerful canary, the very symbol of all cage birds, did not appear on the scene until the 16th Century, when seamen brought it from the Canary Islands to Europe. It proved to be as plastic as the jungle fowl and the rock dove, and selective breeding soon produced a variety of forms while training developed some very accomplished singers. To look at the ancestral canary, a streaky olive-drab bird, and to hear it sing, one might think that the ordinary chaffinch of Europe would have been more promising material to work with.

It was not until the years after World War II that the supremacy of the canary was challenged by another cage bird, the little shell parakeet, or budgerigar. The millions in captivity now probably exceed the hordes that still throng the water holes of Australia's arid hinterland. In captivity they range from clear yellow to blue, but the wild ones are always green.

Aviculturists have multiplied even though protective laws in North America and in many countries of Europe prohibit them from cherishing, behind bars, most of the wild birds of their own countryside. So great has been the demand for some of the more attractive birds of faraway places that Kenya and other tropical countries have had to tighten their restrictions. The ornithologists and the fast-growing army of bird watchers, who prefer their birds wild and free to come and go, do not always see eye to eye with the cage bird clan. They contend that it contradicts the meaning of birds to possess them.

The most valuable wild bird in the world is certainly the guanay cormorant of coastal Peru. Although it cannot match the domestic fowl as a source of revenue, the value of its excrement amounts to millions of dollars every year. The Incas had long used the rich nitrates for fertilizer but it was not until the 19th Century that commercial exploitation made itself felt. Mountains of guano 150 feet (46 m) deep, the accumulation of at least 25 centuries, were mined and shipped away. During the third quarter of the 19th Century Peru shipped 20 million tons (18 million t) of guano worth two billion dollars. With the depletion of the ancient reserves came sober management. The birds are now

JOHN JAMES AUDUBON

Audubon (1785-1851), artist and naturalist, studied with the eminent painter David before leaving France to live in America. His fame rests on his great folio of 435 plates, which were painted with unprecedented naturalness and accuracy from just-killed bird specimens.

JOHN GOULD

Gould (1804-1881), who gained his reputation originally as a taxidermist, later became the leading bird illustrator of England. His first studies of Himalayan birds and hummingbirds, and his monumental "Birds of Europe," made a lasting contribution to the field of ornithology.

guarded, harvesting is regulated and new colonies are encouraged by platforms and retaining walls, all of which has resulted in an increment in the excrement.

Unbridled in their destruction, however, were the Mediterranean peoples who reduced the almost countless migratory quail to their present low level. These are the birds that saved the children of Israel from starvation, as related in Exodus, and it has been estimated by one researcher that in two days and one night they must have killed some nine million quail. But it was commercial exploitation and lack of conservation practices in more recent times that destroyed the big flocks. Prior to 1920 the Egyptians alone, in addition to home consumption, were exporting up to three million birds each year.

The modern philosophy that governs hunting is to crop the annual surplus but not dig into capital—to take the natural increase but not the "seed stock." Accompanying the much-publicized population explosion of the human race has come increasing gun pressure, as well as pressure to add certain species to the game list. It is regrettable that the sandhill crane, a bird that lays but two eggs, is still allowed to be hunted in some parts of the United States and Canada. Shore birds, with their low reproductive potential (usually four eggs) and vulnerable migration lanes, were finally placed under protection, but not before the Eskimo curlew was brought to the very brink of extinction.

WATERFOWL, despite the fact that they lay large clutches and recover quickly from disaster if given a chance, face a future that looks far from bright. Unlike grouse, pheasants and quail, which can spread themselves over hundreds of millions of acres, they must concentrate where the water is. But because governmental and private organizations have established controls over hunting, sportsmen continue to find plenty of waterfowl to bag. During the 1974-1975 hunting season, an estimated 14,322,400 ducks and geese were killed and retrieved by hunters in the United States.

We can do no more than guess at the original duck population of North America. Estimates run between 250 and 500 million. When the pioneer trapper Jim Bridger paddled his buffalo-skin canoe down the Bear River to Great Salt Lake in 1824, ducks darkened the sky in numbers this continent will never see again. He was soon followed by the market gunners who had already decimated the flocks in the East. In 1887 one gunner shot 1,880 birds in a season—another bagged 335 in one day.

The decline of the ducks, however, was not due solely to the gun, nor is it today. Virtually every day plans were made somewhere to drain another pond, swamp or marsh, until about 50 million acres (20 million ha) of the original 127 million acres (51 million ha) of wetland in the United States had disappeared and others were crisscrossed with mosquito-control ditches. In the duck-rich prairie provinces of Canada innumerable nesting places were drained, diminishing the duck crop at its source. The dry cycle that created the Dust Bowl in the late 1920s had a disastrous effect on waterfowl. By 1935 the U.S. Fish and Wildlife Service estimated a continental population of only 27 million birds. It was during the Depression that the great federal refuge program of the United States got started. Today there are about 300 refuges specifically for waterfowl, covering more than four million acres (1.6 million ha). In years when the duck prairies are in the grip of drought, with lake bottoms blowing away in dust, the number of ducks falls heavily; when rains return the number grows again.

In an overcrowded world some forms of hunting, in the opinion of many conservationists, are rapidly becoming impractical and archaic and must eventually be replaced by just looking. How many people content themselves with looking at birds it is difficult to say, for they do not require licenses. Once, when a survey was made at a Midwestern goose marsh, it was revealed that the goose hunters were outnumbered more than 100 to one by people who came just to see the geese.

As the human population soars above the four-billion mark, the clashes between birds and men are certain to become more frequent. The federal government is faced with many requests to control red-winged blackbirds, grackles and other seed-eating species that are having population explosions of their own—largely because they have adapted to changes in man's use of the land and now consider the vast wheatfields and cornfields as theirs to feed in. The growing army of people who like birds will not hear of such violent methods of control as poisoning, dynamiting or shooting, contending rightly that these methods are not selective enough and that other ways must be found to discourage bird depredations.

Birds have their own diseases, which they transmit to other birds, but most of their maladies and their parasites do not affect man. Ornithosis, a sort of viral pneumonia harbored by birds (and once called psittacosis because it was thought to be a disease of parrots) can be transmitted to man by pigeons. But the ornithosis virus is not exclusive to birds—it has been discovered in fur seals of the Bering Sea.

Among the most serious of the arthropod-borne viruses are several forms of encephalitis, or sleeping sickness, and it has been found that birds that are bitten by mosquitoes or ticks often act as a reservoir of contagion. Thus when an outbreak occurs, the cry may go up to get rid of the birds, but this is clearly not practical. For one thing, the greatest offenders may be domestic fowl, penned ducks and pheasants. But even if it were possible to eliminate all birds, wild and domestic, other vertebrate animals also can store the virus and infect humans. The problem must be handled in other ways and biologists and epidemiologists, working together, are seeking the answers.

W HAT of the future of birds? Taking the long, evolutionary view, we might surmise that some birds may go out of the picture, not simply because modern man has made an ecological nuisance of himself, eliminating their habitat, the source of their livelihood, but because they have reached a cul-de-sac, a dead end out of the main stream of life in a changing world. This could be the predicament of the California condor. With a surviving population of some two score individuals, this is the last descendant of the giant scavenger that flourished in North America during the Pleistocene, when mammals were bigger and more abundant than they are today.

Sixty or 70 million years ago, judging by the fossil evidence, the Gruiformes (cranes, rails, bustards and their relatives) made up a far larger part of the world's avifauna than they do today. In addition, they have also declined faster in historic times than any other major order. But whereas the cranes and certain other orders of large birds—the ostrich, the other ratites, and the pelican-like birds—may be slowly losing ground, the perching birds, which make up more than three fifths of all the world's birds, seem to have had their greatest proliferation within the past 10 million years, since the early Pliocene.

Among the perching birds, the seedeaters—the weaverbirds, sparrows, finches and their allies—are the most numerous and perhaps the most plastic. They came into their own relatively recently when seed-bearing plants,

A PLURALITY OF BIRDS

Over the years men have coined a host of special terms to describe birds in groups. Here are some that still survive in the English language.

a siege of herons or bitterns
a plump of wildfowl
a gaggle of geese
a skein of geese (flying)
a herd of swans, cranes or curlews
a badelyng of ducks
a sord (or sute) of mallards
a spring of teal
a company of wigeon
a cast of hawks
a bevy of quail
a covey of partridges
a muster of peacocks
a nye of pheasants
a brood of chickens
a covert of coots
a congregation of plovers
a desert of lapwings
a wisp (or walk) of snipe
a fall of woodcock
a bazaar of murres (guillemots)
a flight of doves or swallows
a murmuration of starlings
an exaltation of larks
a watch of nightingales
a building of rooks
a chattering of choughs
a host of sparrows

especially grasses and sedges, had their great spread. It has been suggested that of all birds they probably have the most promising future, but equal claims could be made for the insect eaters or the nectar feeders. They are all in the same business, evolving along with the flowering plants.

If the average turnover, the life of a species, is about 500,000 years, as Pierce Brodkorb estimated for the Pleistocene, the rate of extinction and replacement in the evolutionary sense should not be more than two species per century. If we accept Brodkorb's yardstick the world should have lost during the past three centuries, since the twilight of the dodo, five or six species through no fault of our own. Indeed, the Labrador duck might well have been one of these, for we cannot truly blame its disappearance on any known human activity.

However, since 1600, we have lost nearly 90 species, some of which are not even represented by a specimen in any of the world's museums. Extinction, if we use Brodkorb's measure, has thus proceeded at about 15 times the evolutionary pace. (James Fisher, assuming a more telescoped time scale in recent millennia, felt that this estimate was excessive, but admitted that man-induced extinction may have been as much as four times as great as it would have been had nature gone its own course.) The years of greatest loss were around the turn of the century. In the 20 years between 1885 and 1905, some 20 species became extinct. Most of the extinctions were among island birds, for they are more vulnerable than continental species. Some, like the dodo and the great auk, being unable to fly, were ruthlessly killed off; others disappeared because of the introduction of rats, goats, cats, rabbits and the mongoose, satellites of man which have swept island after island like a scourge. Still others went out when their special environments were destroyed for agricultural use. Not a small number, such as some of the famous Hawaiian honey creepers, disappeared very mysteriously, but there is evidence that many succumbed to diseases carried by mosquitoes and by introduced birds—bird malaria and bird sleeping sickness. These are diseases to which the invaders might well have built up a tolerance, but which the native birds could not throw off any more than the native Polynesians could survive the ravages of measles and other "harmless" diseases brought by Captain Cook and other early infection-carrying visitors to their islands.

N ORTH AMERICA has lost the great auk, Labrador duck, Carolina parakeet, passenger pigeon and the heath hen, a subspecies of the prairie chicken. But Europe, settled more slowly, has not lost a single mainland species in historic times (the great auk was an island bird). Normally, birds of continental range can cushion the shock of the invader and survive somewhere in the hinterland, perhaps adapting in time; but birds of the islands when pressed soon have their backs to the sea.

A few other birds are so close to extinction that we cannot be sure whether they will survive from one decade to the next. The International Union for Conservation of Nature and Natural Resources' roster estimated in 1977 a worldwide total of 410 endangered species. We have already mentioned some of them in the U.S. and Canada—the ivory-billed woodpecker, the Eskimo curlew, the whooping crane and the California condor. Elsewhere in the world, the short-tailed albatross is making a slow recovery after having been all but wiped out on Japan's Torishima Island; the noisy scrub bird of Australia, the cahow of Bermuda and the notornis of New Zealand, all on the brink of the void, are now under rigid protection after recent rediscovery.

GONE WITH THE WIND

GREAT AUK

The great auk, first bird recorded extinct in the Western Hemisphere, was a goose-sized island dweller of the North Atlantic. Although flightless, it was an excellent swimmer and could have survived indefinitely had it not been ruthlessly hunted by men over a period of 300 years. The last known specimens, a breeding pair, were killed in Iceland in 1844.

LABRADOR DUCK

Little is known about the disappearance of the Labrador duck. Its numbers were apparently small to begin with; then, between 1850 and 1870, it dwindled and vanished. During that time it was hunted, but not excessively. Whether disease, shooting or the loss of some vital food caused its extinction has never been determined, and almost certainly never will be.

There is a finality about extinction. We can very often place a precise date on the disappearance of a bird, but we cannot do the same with an emergent species; it takes its time. That is why the experts often disagree as to whether a bird is a "good" species (i.e., reproductively isolated) or worthy only of subspecific rank.

Alexander Wilson, the father of American ornithology, anticipated more than 150 years ago that the ivory-billed woodpecker, dependent on primeval wilderness, would disappear. He intimated that the other crow-sized woodpecker, the pileated, would follow it, but in this he erred. The genetic stock that could exist in cut-over forest survived to replenish areas that had not heard the loud tapping of the "logcock" in more than a generation. Today it is again a fairly common bird.

The birds that could adapt to gardens, towns, orchards, roadsides and farms are the ones that have prospered most—robins, song sparrows, chipping sparrows, yellow warblers, house wrens, mockingbirds, cardinals, blue jays, meadowlarks, orioles, grackles, kingbirds, phoebes and at least two or three dozen others. The swallows, as a family, have completely accepted man as a benefactor: Barn swallows and cliff swallows prefer his barns and bridges to the cliffs and caves they formerly used; tree swallows and purple martins use his bird boxes; and bank swallows colonize the sand quarries and road cuts. Swifts find chimneys preferable to hollow trees; nighthawks lay their eggs on the flat roofs of office buildings; and so we might go on down the list of successfully integrated bird neighbors.

It is quite certain that as our cities mature the shade trees and gardens will harbor more birds, not fewer. In England, an older country, the highest densities of birds, as we have seen, are in suburban gardens and estates, averaging about 30 birds per acre (0.4 ha), far more than optimum woodland densities.

We need not worry about the future of most songbirds, provided we do not exterminate them with chemical insecticides. The birds that will need our indulgence most are those that require ample living space, like the bald eagle and other birds that have very special requirements.

It is ironic that the most abundant wild bird the world has ever known should have become the very symbol of extinction. The passenger pigeon, estimated to number perhaps five billion in the days of Audubon and Wilson, had a population nearly as great as that of all other breeding land birds in the United States combined. Although the last wild bird was shot in March 1900, a few lived on in captivity until Martha, the lone survivor, died in the Cincinnati Zoo on September 1, 1914, at 1 p.m. Central Standard Time.

Since the beginning of the century, when the slaughter of the commercially prized plume birds and the murder of Guy Bradley, the Audubon warden who sought to stop it, had become a national shame, America has set an example to the world for its progress in bird protection. No country has better protective laws, more bird clubs, more graduate students seeking degrees in ornithology, more millions of acres set aside as refuges, or spends more money each year for conservation.

Throughout the rest of the world, the pattern of bird awareness and protection is uneven. Whereas it is strong in the United States and Canada, in some of the Latin American countries it is almost nonexistent. This ethnic division finds a parallel in western Europe, where bird watching is popular in such places as England, Holland, Germany and Scandinavia, but not in the

CAROLINA PARAKEET

This bird, the only parrot native to the United States, was also a victim of man's predation. A habit of twisting green fruit off the trees led to its widespread destruction as a nuisance. As the country was settled, its original wide range, extending throughout the southern states, steadily contracted, and a flock of 30 in Florida, in 1920, was the last that was ever seen.

HEATH HEN

The last heath hen, a mateless male, died on Martha's Vineyard, Mass., in 1932. Once plentiful around New York and southern New England, this bird could not survive coexistence with men. The settling of the land, plus wholesale shooting for the market, helped decimate it during the end of the 19th Century. Stringent measures to protect it came too late.

Mediterranean basin, where people appreciate birds more in the cage or in the skillet. Among eastern peoples the interest in birds and their conservation reaches its nadir in the Arab countries and its highest degree of development in progressive Japan.

Even in the United States, policy and regulations with respect to birds have been contradictory at the very best. As Dr. Joseph J. Hickey of the University of Wisconsin pointed out: "Without a permit you cannot pick up and take home a car-killed Baltimore oriole, but you can, generally with impunity, cut down a tree containing an oriole nest full of young. You cannot shoot a snowy egret, but you can drain off a marsh on which a whole colony of egret nestlings may depend for food. You cannot shoot a robin, but you can kill it with insecticides."

This inconsistency became tragically clear in the years following World War II, when indiscriminate use of pesticides sometimes led to disastrous consequences. Hickey estimated that up to one half million native robins were killed when large quantities of DDT were used in an effort to save the elm trees of the Middle West. The new pesticides—foremost among them DDT—brought dramatic benefits in increased world food production and played an important role in fighting arthropod-borne diseases such as malaria, yellow fever, dengue fever and filariasis. But the virtues of these new pesticides—their ability to kill pests across a broad spectrum, and their chemical stability—proved to be a curse. They are so stable they do not break down chemically after they are exposed to weather or even after they are eaten. They persist, to spread through food chains and ecosystems.

P ARTICULARLY in water environments, the chemicals are concentrated by the natural operation of the food chain. Rain washes them into ponds and streams, where they are absorbed by plankton. Minnows eat the plankton, larger fish the minnows, and birds of prey the larger fish. The effect on several species of predatory birds has been disastrous; populations of the bald eagle and the osprey, both fisheaters, declined drastically during the 1950s and 1960s along the Atlantic coast. Their disappearance was noted with alarm, but the role played by pesticides remained mysterious—the concentration of chemicals in the bodies of many of the affected birds was too low to kill them. Finally, investigators discovered that DDT, in particular, altered the reproduction process, causing the laying of sterile eggs or eggs with shells so thin that they broke before chicks could hatch.

Public outcry led to governmental action in the United States. The general use of DDT was banned in 1972, although it has been applied for certain limited purposes there and has continued to be used in other parts of the world. Strict controls were placed over other pesticides in the U.S., and most of those in use were nonpersistent—that is, while poisonous in their original form, after use they quickly decomposed into innocuous compounds.

The birds of prey are returning gradually. But the danger cannot be forgotten. Some species populations remain precariously small. Pesticides and other pollutants are still a hazard, for their long-term effects seldom can be predicted. However, the need for vigilance seems accepted. Once having narrowly averted the accidental extinction of prized creatures, man apparently concluded that to stay at the top of the food chain himself, he has to safeguard every link. Certainly a world without birds or a spring without song would be incomplete for anyone; for many it would be intolerable.

OSTRICHES RUN ACROSS A ROCK IN THE SAHARA, PRESERVED FOR THE AGES BY SOME STONE AGE ARTIST AT LEAST 10,000 YEARS AGO

Man, the Admiring Enemy

Man's association with birds has always been peculiarly intimate, if one-sided. He has worshiped birds, used them as symbols in his art, hunted them for food and plumage, and seen some 90 species disappear in modern times. But while exploiting them, he has also defended them. Today, with birds threatened as never before, he is helping some of them with their greatest problem: living with man.

IN A SCENE FAMILIAR TO HUNTERS, AN EGYPTIAN MURAL SHOWS DUCKS TAKING WING, TWO HIT BY STICKS, AND A HERON DECOY (LEFT)

Birds as Gods and Symbols

In ancient civilizations, birds were symbols often raised to the rank of deities. Probably the original bird god was the Garuda, a great, golden-winged mythical eagle of Asia, "the bird of life, destroyer of all, creator of all." The Babylonians and the Hittites built temples to eagles. The strongest deity of the Egyptian pantheon was Horus, a falcon. Minor Egyptian gods, both benevolent and evil, were also represented in bird form, like the pintails shown above in a detail from a 15th Century B.C. tomb. The ducks being flushed from a papyrus marsh symbolize demons which are ritually struck down by throwing sticks carved in the shape of serpents. Other birds were also given supernatural powers in many societies: The priests of Rome considered it a bad omen before a battle if the sacred chickens showed little appetite for their ceremonial grain.

THE WISE OLD OWL was first so named by the Greeks, who pictured it as the companion of Athene, goddess of wisdom. Here an owl appears on an Athenian coin of the Fifth Century B.C.

A HAWAIIAN WAR IDOL IS DECORATED WITH RED IIWI FEATHERS AND BLACK OO FEATHERS

The Toll of Oil Spills

Throughout history man has killed wild birds for their meat or their plumage. Not until modern times has he killed millions by accident. These birds are the victims of giant industrial mishaps, felled when damaged oil tankers have leaked their cargo onto a stretch of coast.

Not much can be done to save flocks of blackened, panicky birds struggling to flee an oil spill. The oil reduces their body insulation, and many are so chilled they die of pneumonia. Others are poisoned by the oil consumed as they try to preen themselves clean. Rescuers rinse them with detergents, but these caustic solutions may burn the skin. Often men can only set off firecrackers to scare unharmed birds away from a spill.

A large oil spill—and there were at least seven during a month-long period in 1975—may kill a hundred thousand birds outright. But many more must be reckoned as casualties, since even small doses of oil injure a bird's reproductive organs.

A DAZED GREBE is swaddled and gently swabbed at a rescue station. Many wild birds, unaccustomed to being handled, die of shock in the arms of volunteers trying to clean them.

SHIVERING RUDDY DUCKS are force-fed liquid protein by a rescue worker. They have already been rinsed, dried and purged of any oil they may have swallowed. The staff of this station in Delaware cleaned, nursed and fed 270 ducks and geese that had been caught in a serious oil spill in the Delaware River. Only 28 of the birds were alive four weeks later.

SLICK WITH SPILLED OIL, THIS WESTERN GREBE HAS VERY LITTLE CHANCE OF SURVIVAL

Rescuing Birds of Prey

The majestic North American birds of prey—the owls, eagles and hawks—have almost no natural enemies but man. His traps and guns kill many, but after World War II the hawk and eagle succumbed to an even more insidious depredation. The pesticide DDT concentrated in their bodies and harmed their reproductive systems. The eggs were infertile or so thin-shelled that the weight of a brooding parent could crush them. Peregrine falcons were among the hardest hit. When general use of DDT was ended in the United States in 1972, the peregrine population had been reduced from several thousand to only 12 breeding pairs outside of Alaska.

To save the species, falcon lovers began breeding the falcons in captivity—a feat never before accomplished—and then freed the young. Some chicks were slipped into the nests of wild pairs to be raised as foster children. Others were raised by scientists, and then slowly conditioned to fend for themselves. By 1977 more than 180 young falcons had been released. Slowly, as the same techniques were used with other species, wheeling, swooping birds of prey reappeared in American skies.

GREAT HORNED OWL hangs from an Ohio farmer's pole trap, dead of exhaustion. Farmers consider predators a menace, and often thwart all efforts to protect them from extinction.

HUNGRY PEREGRINE CHICKS, less than two weeks out of the incubator, huddle together in a laboratory brooding pan. In several weeks they will be transferred to outdoor quarters.

A CAGE OF YOUNG FALCONS is placed on a high mountain eyrie in New York state. Scientists will leave food for the birds until they have become completely self-sufficient in the wild.

DODOS WERE DRAWN IN 1599 BY A DUTCH ARTIST WHO MAY HAVE HAD SPECIMENS TO COPY. NO COMPLETE SPECIMEN REMAINS TODAY

IGNORANCE about dodos is revealed by these drawings which agree only on heavy body, big bill and feet.

The Ultimate Doom

The peregrine falcon is a bird that may eventually recover from the ravages of man. The Mauritius dodo and the American passenger pigeon are two that did not. The dodo, the first bird to become extinct in modern times, was doomed by inability to fly when man brought pigs and rats to Mauritius in the 16th Century. Much of its life and habits are a mystery, but it was a sluggish bird, easy prey for these hunters and eaters of its eggs. The last dodo vanished late in the 17th Century.

The passenger pigeon died more quickly and more ominously. Early in the 19th Century, North America still supported three to five billion of these birds, far more than any other species on the continent. They were esteemed for their delicate flavor; their crowded nesting grounds and communal flights made them easy prey to wholesale shooting and netting. By 1880 it was already too late to save them. The last wild passenger pigeon was shot in 1900; the last of them all died in captivity in 1914.

MARTHA
last of her species, died at 1:00 p.m.,
1 September 1914, age 29, in the
Cincinnati Zoological Gardens.

EXTINCT

THE END OF A SPECIES that used to darken American skies with flocks of millions came on September 1, 1914, when Martha, the last passenger pigeon, died in the Cincinnati Zoo. Her stuffed body is now in the National Museum in Washington *(above)*, a sad reminder that once a species begins to die out, the dying may snowball at a rate that even an aroused public cannot stop.

THE MOST MAJESTIC bird in America, a whooping crane may exceed five feet (1.5 m) and have a seven-foot (2.1-m) wing span.

On the Brink of Extinction

The extinction of the passenger pigeon dramatized what ornithologists have by now bitterly learned: Many birds cannot adjust to man. If such species are to survive, man must adjust to them and take active, even drastic measures to protect them.

A case in point is the whooping crane. This big, aristocratic bird—named for its loud, bugle-like call and famous for its graceful mating dance—once flew in large numbers from its winter retreat on the Gulf of Mexico to its breeding grounds on the Great Plains. It built grass nests one or two feet (0.3 to 0.6 m) high in marshes and shallow lakes. But with man's surge westward from 1800 to 1900, whoopers were crowded out of their breeding areas. Many swamps where they nested were drained.

ONE DAY OLD, A BABY WHOOPING CRANE IN THE NEW ORLEANS AUDUBON PARK ZOO IS FED INSECTS BY ITS PARENTS. A FULL-GROWN CRANE

Many migrating cranes were indiscriminately shot. By 1889 they had deserted their last Minnesota nesting sites and by 1940 only a pitiful 15 birds wintered in the coastal marshes of Texas. No one knew where they laid their eggs.

Then, in 1955, they were found nesting in northern Alberta, Canada. Between 1971 and 1975 their number fell from 61 to 49. Finally, in an attempt to increase their numbers and prevent a disaster from wiping out the entire remaining wild flock, a number of whooping-crane eggs were taken from their nests and placed with sandhill-crane foster parents. In 1975 and 1976 eight young whooping cranes raised by sandhills migrated with their new family. The future seemed brighter for the whooping crane.

HAS A DIET THAT INCLUDES WORMS, FROGS, SNAKES AND SHELLFISH

SIX WEEKS OLD, a baby whooping crane's immature body perches unsteadily on stiltlike legs. As an adult its windpipe will be trumpeting a cry that can be heard for two miles (3.2 km).

A Helpful Hand for Storks

The European stork, traditional baby-deliverer for people, is not maintaining its own population. Long a fixture of European towns, nesting on chimneys and steeples, the stork is now declining. Holland had 312 breeding couples in 1939, only eight in 1974. Switzerland had 150 couples in 1900; in 1974, none. Since then the Swiss have had some success raising Algerian white storks.

No one is sure why the storks' survival rate is dropping, though it may be the growing use of insecticides in South Africa, where the storks migrate to feed on insects in winter. But whatever the cause, the bird lovers of Alsace, where the stork is a symbol of good luck, determined to preserve the birds. They organized to help the storks and called in ornithologists to teach villagers to build and renovate nests. In time they had at least 10 pairs of wild storks raising young in the nests.

A similar dedication to the preservation of birds is growing in many lands. Wildlife conservation has become much more urgent with the spread of metropolitan areas. In North America, where four species have died out since the white man came, four to five million bird watchers are now concerned with the protection of the 650 species that still breed there.

MAN-MADE NEST, on the unfinished roof of Ilhaeusern church in Alsace, was built for storks by the villagers when the church was rebuilt from the rubble of war. Storks return to it year after year to raise families.

WORK OF PRESERVATION in Alsace includes building nests (*left*), care and feeding of stork chicks hatched in incubators by local protectionists and even propagation of their favorite local food, frogs. The sign above, hung in restaurants of the area, requests diners not to ask for frogs' legs but to please "leave this delicacy for our young"—and is signed "the storks of Alsace."

AT DAWN IN WASHINGTON, D.C., ORNITHOLOGISTS BEGIN A BIRD COUNT. THE AUTHOR IS SECOND FROM LEFT

Bibliography

Biology of Birds, General

Dorst, Jean, *The Life of Birds* (2 vols.). Columbia University Press, 1974.

Farner, Donald S., and James R. King, *Avian Biology* (5 vols.). Academic Press, 1971-1975.

Fisher, James, and Roger Tory Peterson, *The World of Birds*. Doubleday, 1964.

Pettingill, Olin S., Jr., *Ornithology in Laboratory and Field*. Burgess, 1970.

Van Tyne, J., and A. J. Berger, *Fundamentals of Ornithology*. Wiley, 1976.

Welty, Joel Carl, *The Life of Birds*. Saunders, 1975.

Evolution and Classification

American Ornithologists' Union, *Check-list of North American Birds* (5th ed., 3rd printing), 1975 (32nd and 33rd supplements 1973, 1975).

Austin, Oliver L., Jr., and Arthur Singer, *Birds of the World*. Golden Press, 1961.

Edwards, Ernest P., *A Coded List of Birds of the World*. Ernest P. Edwards, 1974.

Meyer de Schauensee, Rudolphe, *The Species of Birds of South America and Their Distribution*. Livingston, 1966.

Morony, John, Jr., Walter Bock and John Farrand Jr., *Reference List of Birds of the World*. American Museum of Natural History, 1975.

Peters, J. L., *Check-list of Birds of the World* (13 vols.). Harvard University Press, 1931-1977.

Ridgway, R., and H. Friedmann, *Birds of North and Middle America* (11 vols.). U.S. National Museum, 1901-1950.

Vaurie, Charles, *The Birds of the Palaearctic Fauna* (Vols. I and II). Witherby, 1959-1965.

Wetmore, Alexander, *A Checklist of the Fossil and Prehistoric Birds of North America and the West Indies*. Smithsonian Miscellaneous Collection 131 (5): 1956. *A Classification for the Birds of the World*. (Vol. 139). Smithsonian Miscellaneous Collection, 1960.

Regional Books and Guides

Alexander, W. B., *Birds of the Ocean*. Putnam, 1963.

Ali, Salim, and S. Dillon Ripley, *Handbook of the Birds of India and Pakistan* (10 vols.). Oxford University Press, 1968-1974.

Bond, James, *Birds of the West Indies* (4th ed.). Houghton Mifflin, 1974.

Dement'ev, G. P., and N. A. Gladkov, *Birds of the Soviet Union* (6 vols.). Israel Program for Scientific Translation, 1966-1970.

Heinzel, Hermann, Richard Fitter and John Parslow, *The Birds of Britain and Europe with North Africa and the Middle East*. Collins, 1972.

MacDonald, James D., *Birds of Australia*. Witherby, 1973.

MackWorth-Praed, C. W., and C. H. B. Grant, *African Handbook of Birds* (6 vols.). Longmans Green, 1952-1973.

Meyer de Schauensee, Rudolphe, *A Guide to the Birds of South America*. Livingston, 1970.

Palmer, Ralph, *Handbook of North American Birds* (3 vols.). Yale University Press, 1962, 1976.

Peterson, Roger Tory, *A Field Guide to the Birds*. Houghton Mifflin, 1947. *A Field Guide to Western Birds*. Houghton Mifflin, 1941.

Peterson, Roger Tory, and Edward L. Chalif, *Field Guide to Mexican Birds*. Houghton Mifflin, 1973.

Peterson, R. T., G. Mountfort and P. A. D. Hollom, *A Field Guide to the Birds of Britain and Europe*. Houghton Mifflin, 1954.

Robbins, Chandler, Bertel Bruun, Herbert S. Zim and Arthur B. Singer, *Birds of North America*. Golden Press, 1966.

Serventy, D. L., V. Serventy and J. Warham, *The Handbook of Australian Sea-birds*. Reed, 1971.

Voous, Karel H., *Atlas of European Birds*. Nelson, 1960.

Watson, George E., *Birds of the Antarctic and Sub-Antarctic*. American Geophysical Union, 1975.

Witherby, H. F., ed., *The Handbook of British Birds* (5 vols.). Witherby, 1938-1941.

Life Histories

Bannerman, David A., *The Birds of the British Isles* (12 vols.). Oliver and Boyd, 1953-1963.

Bent, Arthur C., *Life Histories of North American Birds* (23 vols.). Dover, 1919-1968.

Brown, Leslie, and Dean Amadon, *Eagles, Hawks, and Falcons of the World*. Hamlyn, 1968.

Burton, John A., ed., *Owls of the World*. E. P. Dutton, 1973.

Delacour, J., *The Waterfowl of the World* (3 vols.). Country Life, 1954-1959.

Farner, Donald S., ed., *Breeding Biology of Birds*. National Academy of Sciences, 1973.

Fisher, James, and R. M. Lockley, *Seabirds*. Houghton Mifflin, 1954.

Greenewalt, Crawford H., *Hummingbirds*. Doubleday, 1960.

Harrison, Hal H., *A Field Guide to Birds' Nests*. Houghton Mifflin, 1975.

Johnsgard, Paul A., *Waterfowl of North America*. Indiana University Press, 1975.

Lack, David, *Darwin's Finches*. Cambridge University Press, 1947. *The Life of the Robin*. Witherby, 1943.

Lockley, R., *Shearwaters*. J. N. Dent & Sons, 1942.

Murphy, R. C., *Oceanic Birds of South America* (2 vols.). American Museum of Natural History, 1936.

Skutch, A. F., *Life Histories of Central American Birds* (3 vols.). Cooper Ornithological Society, 1954-1969.

Stout, Gardner (ed.), text by Peter Matthiessen, *The Shorebirds of North America*. Viking Press, 1967.

Behavior and Communication

Armstrong, Edward A., *A Study of Bird Song*. Oxford University Press, 1963. *Bird Display and Behavior*. Oxford University Press, 1947.

Cornell Laboratory of Ornithology, *A Field Guide to Bird Songs; A Field Guide to Western Bird Songs* and numerous other recordings. Houghton Mifflin, 1959, 1971.

Greenewalt, Crawford H., *Bird Song: Acoustics and Physiology*. Smithsonian Institution Press, 1968.

Hartshorne, Charles, *Born to Sing*. Indiana University Press, 1973.

Hinde, R. A., ed., *Bird Vocalizations*. Cambridge University Press, 1969.

Howard, H. E., *Territory in Bird Life*. Collins, 1948.

Kendeigh, S. C., *Parental Care and Its Evolution in Birds*. Illinois Biological Monographs 22: (1-3), 1952.

Lanyon, W. E., and W. N. Tavolga, *Animal Sounds and Communication*. American Institute of Biological Sciences, 1960.

Lorenz, Konrad, *King Solomon's Ring*. Crowell, 1952.

Saunders, Aretas A., *A Guide to Bird Songs*. Doubleday, 1951.

Thorpe, William H., *Bird Song*. Cambridge University Press, 1961. *Learning and Instinct in Animals*. Harvard University Press, 1956.

Tinbergen, Nikolaas, *Bird Life*. Oxford University Press, 1954. *The Herring Gull's World*. Collins, 1953.

Flight and Migration

Dorst, Jean, *The Migrations of Birds*. Houghton Mifflin, 1962.

Griffin, Donald R., *Bird Migration*. Dover, 1974.

Hochbaum, H. Albert, *Travels and Traditions of Waterfowl*. University of Minnesota Press, 1955.

Matthews, G. V. T., *Bird Navigation*. Cambridge University Press, 1968.

Moreau, R. E., *The Palaearctic-African Bird Migration Systems*. Academic Press, 1972.

Pennycuick, C. J., *Animal Flight*. Arnold, London, 1972.

Population Ecology

Cody, Martin L., *Competition and Structure of Bird Communities*. Princeton University Press, 1974.

Lack, David, *Ecological Isolation in Birds*. Harvard University Press, 1971. *Population Studies of Birds*. Clarendon Press, Oxford, 1966.

Wynne-Edwards, V. C., *Animal Dispersion in Relation to Social Behavior*. Oliver and Boyd, 1962.

Conservation

Matthiessen, Peter, *Wildlife in America*. Viking Press, 1959.

Murton, Ronald K., *Man and Birds*. Taplinger, 1972.

Murton, R. K., and E. W. Wright, *The Problems of Birds as Pests*. Academic Press, 1968.

Zimmerman, David R., *To Save a Bird in Peril*. Coward, McCann and Geoghegan, 1975.

CREDITS

Credits for pictures from left to right are separated by commas, top to bottom by dashes.

PHOTOGRAPHS—Cover: Robert B. Goodman from Black Star. 17: Georg Nystrand from Frank Lane. 20: Robert B. Goodman from Black Star. 21: Cy La Tour. 22: Ron Austing from Photo Researchers, Inc.—Constance P. Warner. 23: John Markham. 24, 25: Dmitri Kessel. 26, 27: N. R. Farbman, Jerry Cooke from Photo Researchers, Inc., John Markham from Photo Researchers, Inc. 28: John Markham. 29: Christina Loke from *Birds in the Sun* by Malcolm MacDonald from Photo Researchers, Inc. 30, 31: John Markham from Photo Researchers, Inc. 32: Robert B. Goodman from Black Star. 41: Andreas Feininger. 46, 47: Andreas Feininger. 48: Tokutaro Tanaka. 49: Martin Iger for SPORTS ILLUSTRATED. 50, 51: Constance P. Warner. 52: R. Van Nostrand from National Audubon Society. 53: Lilo Hess except top left; Marie Hansen. 54: Rene-Pierre Bille except top; Leon D. Harmon from Photo Researchers, Inc. 55: Hans W. Silvester. 56: J. Bristol Foster. 66, 67: Kurt Severin. 68: Hermann Schunemann from Annan Photo Service except bottom; Heinz Sielmann. 69: Christina Loke from *Birds in the Sun* by Malcolm MacDonald from Photo Researchers, Inc. 70 through 73: Shelly Grossman. 74, 75: Fritz Goro, James Simon from Photo Researchers, Inc.—Roger Tory Peterson—Maitland A. Edey. 76: Constance P. Warner. 78: John G. Zimmerman. 89, 92: Eric Hosking from Photo Researchers, Inc. 93: Roger Tory Peterson. 94, 95: Robert Cushman Murphy. 96, 97: Hans W. Silvester. 98: Eric Schaal. 109: Eric Hosking from Photo Researchers, Inc. 110, 111: James Whitmore. 112, 113: Stephen T. Emlen, David Hamilton. 113: Ralph Morse from *Scientific American,* December 1974—Charles Walcott. 114: D. G. Smith. 115: William J. Johoda from National Audubon Society, J. R. Eyerman—Albert Fenn. 116, 117: Leonard McCombe. 118: David Goodnow. 120: Leonard W. Wing from *National History of Birds, a Guide to Ornithology,* © 1956, The Ronald Press Company—Aretas A. Saunders from *A Guide to Bird Songs,* © 1935 Appleton-Century-Crofts, Inc.—Wesley E. Lanyon, The American Museum of Natural History. 127: Treat Davidson from National Audubon Society. 130, 131: Helen Cruickshank from National Audubon Society. 132, 133: Gary Nuechterlein. 134, 135: Les Line, Ron Ryan—Dr. M. Philip Kahl from Verda International Photos. 136: Walther Rohdich from Annan Photo Service. 147: Christopher Doncaster. 148, 149: Niall Rankin. 150, 151: Warren Roth from Black Star. 152: Gordon A. Ranger courtesy of H. Friedmann—Eric Hosking from Photo Researchers, Inc. 153: John Markham. 154, 155: Jack J. Kunz. 156, 157: Christina Loke from *Birds in the Sun* by Malcolm MacDonald from Photo Researchers, Inc., Loke Wan Tho, Christina Loke from *Birds in the Sun* by Malcolm MacDonald from Photo Researchers, Inc.—William H. Drury Jr., B. Max Thompson from National Audubon Society. 158, 159: Helen Cruickshank from the National Audubon Society, Walter Dawn. 160: Torrey Jackson from Photo Researchers, Inc. 161: L. H. Smith from Len Sirman Press. 162, 163: Russ Kinne from Photo Researchers, Inc., Robert Doisneau from Rapho Guillumette. 164: Alfred Eisenstaedt. 173: Emil Schulthess courtesy Conzett and Huber from Black Star. 174: Abeille document from *Great Centuries of Painting—Egyptian Painting,* editions Skira Geneva—Charles Mohr from National Audubon Society. 175: William Davenport, Yale University. 176: Robert Belous. 177: Jeff Foott from Bruce Coleman, Inc.—Keith Meyer/*The New York Times.* 178: John A. Blakeman from the National Audubon Society Collection/PR. 179: The Peregrine Fund, Heinz Meng, State University of New York. 180: Charles Muskavitch. 181: Noel Clark. 182, 183: Joe Scherschel except top left; Red Moores. 184: Thomas D. McAvoy. 185: Francis Miller.

PAINTINGS AND DRAWINGS—81: Mark A. Binn. 35, 102, 103 (maps), 106, 107: Adolph E. Brotman. 12, 13, 34, 36 through 39, 59, 60, 61, 82, 83, 123, 125: Lois and Louis Darling. 128, 129 (landscape): Ara Derderian. 90, 91: Bill Dove. 8, 42, 43, 44, 45 (ducks based on pen and camera studies by Richard E. Bishop and Edgar M. Queeny in *Prairie Wings*; hummingbirds based on drawings by Dale Astle in *Hummingbirds*), 166, 167: Rudolf Freund. 154, 155: Jack J. Kunz. 15: René Martin. 62, 140, 141: Peter Parnell. 10, 11, 18, 19, 86, 87, 102, 103 (birds), 128, 129 (birds), 143, 144, 145, 170, 171.

Acknowledgments

The editors of the second edition are indebted to: Stephen T. Emlen and William T. Keeton, Section of Neurobiology and Behavior, Cornell University; Donald Kroodsma, Field Research Center, Rockefeller University; James A. Tucker, American Birding Association, Inc. and George E. Watson, Smithsonian Institution.

The editors of the first edition are indebted to: John Aldrich, U.S. Fish and Wildlife Service; Arthur Allen, Cornell University; Dean Amadon, The American Museum of Natural History; Andrew J. Berger, Associate Professor of Anatomy, University of Michigan; Pierce Brodkorb, University of Florida; the late James Chapin, The American Museum of Natural History; Roland C. Clement, Staff Biologist, National Audubon Society; William Conway, New York Zoological Park; Philip A. DuMont and Allan Duvall, U.S. Fish and Wildlife Service; Eugene Eisenmenn, Department of Ornithology, The American Museum of Natural History; the late James Fisher, Director and Chief Editor, Rathbone Books, London; Crawford H. Greenewalt and Doubleday and Co. for permission to use *Hummingbirds* as source for drawings on pages 44 and 45; Mary Heimerdinger, Yale University; Joseph J. Hickey, University of Wisconsin; Peter Paul Kellogg, Cornell University; Jane Kinne, Photo Researchers, Inc.; Wesley E. Lanyon, Robert Cushman Murphy and Charles E. O'Brien, The American Museum of Natural History; Robert J. Newman, Curator, Museum of Zoology, Louisiana State University; Barbara Peterson; A. H. and A. W. Reed, publishers, New Zealand; S. Dillon Ripley, Secretary of the Smithsonian Institution; Charles G. Sibley, Yale University; John H. Storer; Niko Tinbergen, Oxford University, England; Joel Carl Welty, Beloit College; Robert Woodward, National Audubon Society; Rhea Zinman, U.S. Department of Agriculture; the Patuxent Refuge Center, U.S. Fish and Wildlife Service; and the library staffs of The American Museum of Natural History and the National Audubon Society.

Index

Numerals in italics indicate a photograph or painting of the subject mentioned.

Accipiters (bird hawks), 62
Adaptation. *See* Environment, adaptation to; Feeding devices; Flight adaptations; Foot adaptations
Adaptive radiation (divergence), 11-12, 13, 16
Aepyornis. *See* Elephant bird
Aerodynamics, 39-40, *diagrams 42-45*
Africa, bird population densities in, 84-85
Air sacs, 35, 47, 49; of divers, 66
Airports, birds near, 62, 81, 101, 116
Albatross, 14, 146; black-browed, *18-19;* breeding age, 83, 139; classification, 14, 20; courtship, *148-149;* distribution, 14; feeding of young, 159; feet, 38; fertility, 83, 142; flight, 40, *diagrams* 43; Galápagos, 86; incubation, 145; origin of word, 14; royal, 83; short-tailed, 170; wandering, 14, 40, *148-149;* wing design, 40; wing size, 14, 40, *148*
Allen, Arthur, 138
Altricial birds, *144,* 146
Alula, *42*
Anatomy: as basis of classification, 16; similarities with reptiles, 9; skeleton, *13,* 35, *41, 46,* 47. *See also* Flight adaptations; Foot adaptations
Anhinga, 14, 20; bill, *61*
Anseriformes, *18,* 20, *21. See also* Duck; Goose; Swan; Waterfowl
Ant bird, 58
Antarctica, 9, 13, 14, 25, 101
Apodiformes, *19,* 20. *See also* Hummingbird; Swift
Apterygiformes, *18,* 20. *See also* Kiwi
Archaeopteryx, 8, 10, 40, 143; fossil, *8;* mentioned, 11, 12
Archaeornithes, ancestral birds, 10
Arctic, 25, 100
Arena behavior, 124-125
Aristotle, 99
Art, bird depiction in, *173-175*
Audiospectrogram of bird song, *120*
Audubon, John James, 37, 81, 101, 166, *167,* 171
Audubon Breeding Bird Census, 84
Auk: classification, 15, 20, 24; colonies, 83, 85; eggs, 142; fertility, 83; great, extinct, *170;* little, 83; wings, 15. *See also* Murre
Austin, Oliver, Jr., 102
Avocet, 25

Babbler, yellow-eyed, nest of, *157*
Bachman, John, 37
Baker, Stuart, 144
Baltimore oriole, 172
Banding of birds, 102-103, 109, *115*
Barbet, 16, 20, 143, 152; green, *69*
Barbicels, 34
Barbs, 33, *34*
Barbules, 34
Beaks. *See* Bills

Bee-eater, 16, 58; classification, 16, 20, 29; eggs, 143; nests, 29, 140
Beebe, William, 166
Behavior patterns and enigmas, 126, 127, *132-133. See also* Communication; Courtship; Defense; Feeding devices and behavior; Parental care
Bible, mention of birds in, 99, 167, 168
Bills: adaptations, 12, 14, *15,* 37, *59-61,*68, *76-77;* for defense, 76; "duck," 14; functions of, 37, 76; hooked, of predators, 14, 15, *22,* 71, *76;* of hummingbird, *15;* of seedeaters, 59, *60, 76*
Bio-acoustics, 122
Biome concept of distribution, 80-81, *82*
Bird of paradise, 16; arena behavior, 125; egg, *155;* red, *19*
Bird watching, 169, 171-172, *185*
Birds of Europe, Gould, 167
Birds of prey: DDT damage to, 172, 179; diurnal, 14, *22,* 62-63, 70-71, *72-73;* evolution, 11; eyesight, 22, 35, 51; help natural selection, 63; hooked beaks, 14, 15, 62, *70-71;* hooked talons, 14, 15, *22, 38,* 71; method of killing, 62; nocturnal, 14, 15, 62, *70-71;* population cycles, 88; solitary, 119. *See also* Condor; Eagle; Falcon; Hawk; Osprey; Owl; Vulture
Blackbird: abundance and control of, 85, 169; Brewer's, 120; red-winged, 85, 104, 120, 138, 169; tricolored, colonies, 84
Bluebird: migration, 104; nest, 140
Bobolink, *102;* migration, 102, map 103
Bobwhite, *49,* 121, 122, 126
Bock, Walter J., 20
Body heat: normal temperature, 52, 100; regulation by air sacs, 35, 49; regulation by plumage, 34, 53; transformation in newborn, 162
Bones, modification for flight, *13,* 35, *47*
Booby, 14, 64; classification, 14, 20; diving,66; Peruvian, *94-95,* red-footed, *20*
Bowerbird: courtship ritual, 124; satin, eye of, *50*
Bradley, Guy, 171
Brain case, 37
Brant, 62
Breastbone keel, *13,* 35, *46,* 47; lacking in ratites, 12
Breeding. *See* Eggs; Mating; Nest building; Nests; Selective breeding
Breeding age, 83, 139
Bridger, Jim, 168
Broadbill, green, nest of, 141
Brodkorb, Pierce, 11, 170
Brood spots, 145
Brooding, 145, 162. *See also* Incubation
Budgerigar, 26, 167
Buffon, Georges Louis Leclerc de, *166*

Bunting: diet, 59; habitat, *83;* indigo, *83,* 107-108, 139; reed, *109*
Bustard, 15, 20, 169; diet, 58
Buzzard, honey, 63

Cahow, 170
California Fish and Game Department, 116
Call notes, 119, 122-123
Camouflage, *54;* of eggs, 139, 143, 155
Canary, 167
Canvasback, 62, 64
Caprimulgiformes, *19,* 20, *28. See also* Goatsuckers; Nighthawk; Nightjar; Oilbird; Whip-poorwill
Caracara, beak, *76*
Cardinal, 86, 88, 171; northern, egg, *154*
Cariama, 11
Cassowary, 13, *18,* 20; flight-lessness, 12; toenail slashes, 13, 38
Casuariiformes, *18,* 20. *See also* Cassowary; Emu
Censuses of birds, 84-85, 86, map 90-91
Chachalaca, 162
Chaffinch, 86, 120, 167; nest, 140
Chance, Edgar, 144
Chapman, Frank M., 37, 138
Charadriiformes, *18,* 20, *24-25. See also* Auk; Gull; Jacana; Plover; Puffin; Sandpiper; Shore birds; Skimmer, black; Skua; Tern
Chickadee, 38, 123
Chicken, domestic: ancestor, 165; call notes of hens, 123; population, 165; selective breeding, 166
Chiffchaff, call of, *table* 121
Chimango, 143
Ciconiiformes, *19,* 20. *See also* Egret; Flamingo; Heron; Ibis; Spoonbill; Stork
Classification, example of, *table* 16
Classification of birds, 12-16, *18-19, table* 20; basis of, 16, 20; characteristics of class, 9-10; number of living orders and families, 12, 20; representatives of orders, *18-31*
Cleaning relationships, 74, *75*
Cock-of-the-rock, arena behavior, 125
Cockatoo, 20; bill, *60*
Cockfighting, 166
Coliiformes, *19,* 20. *See also* Mousebird
Collias, Nicholas, 122
Colonial birds, *92-97;* colony sizes, 83-84, 89; land, 84, 85, 138; nesting ground densities, 84, 85, 138, 140-141; non-recognition of eggs, 143; reasons for colonizing, 92, 95, 138; sea, 83-84, 85, 89, *92-95,* 138
Coloration: camouflage by, *54;* of eggs, 143, 155; for identification, 120, 121; of nectar and fruit feeders, 60; peacock feather, *52. See also* Courtship plumage
Columbiformes, *18,* 20, *26. See*

also Dodo; Dove; Pigeon; Sandgrouse
Coly, 16. *See also* Mousebird
Communal life. *See* Colonial birds
Communication, 119-126; courtship and rivalry, 120, 122, 123-126, *132-133;* between different species, 123; embryonic, 126; food calls, 122, 123, 126; functions of, 120, 122; means of, 119, 121, 124, *134-135;* during migration, 122-123; vocal *vs.* non-vocal sound, 119; warning cries, 120, 123. *See also* Song
Condor: California, 63, 86, *87,* 88, 169, 170; eggs, 142; flight and landing of, 40
Contour feathers, 34, *53*
Convergence, 16; defined, 13; examples of, 13, 15, 37, 59
Cook, Wells, 84
Coot, 15; classification, 15, 16, 20, 23; egg of American, *154;* European, *23;* feet of, 23, 38
Coraciiformes, *19,* 20, *29. See also* Bee-eater; Hoopoe; Hornbill; Kingfisher; Motmot; Roller
Cormorant, 14, 60; classification, 14, 20; colonies, 85, 95; double-crested, eye of, *51;* eggs, 142; feet, 38; flightless Galápagos, 86; guanay, 61, 95, 167
Cornell University Laboratory of Ornithology, 119
Courtship, 139, *148-149;* arena behavior, 124-125; dance, 124, 125, *132-133, 148-149,* 182; display, *118,* 148; feeding, 120, 123-124, 132, 139; flight, 148; intimidation, 120; plumage, 35, 120, 124, 125, 148; rituals, 120, 123-126, *132-133,* 148; song, 120, 122, 128, 148
Cowbird: bay-winged, 152; parasitism, 143, 144, 152; screaming, 152
Crane, 15, 61, 148, 169; classification, 15, 16, 20,-23; demoiselle, *49;* evolution, 11; lesser sandhill, 86, 168; migration, 99, 106; sandhill, 183; sarus, *135;* whooping, 85-86, 88, 170, *182-183*
Creeper: tree, 58, 123; wood, 58
Cretaceous, 10
Crossbill, 87; bill, *60*
Crow, 64, 123; Bombay house, 157; egg of American, *155;* highly evolved, 16, 31
Cuckoo, 15, 119; black-billed, 144; classification, 15, 20, 27; European, 142, 144, 146, *152;* guira, egg of, *155;* New World, 144; parasitism, 142, 144, *152-153;* yellow-billed, 144
Cuculiformes, *19,* 20, *27. See also* Cuckoo; Touraco
Curassow, 15
Curlew, Eskimo, 85, *86,* 168, 170

Dance rituals, 124, 125, *130-133, 148-149*
Darwin, Charles, 10, 80, 83; and Galápagos finches, 11-12, 58
DDT, 172, 179

188

Defense: by camouflage, 54; instinctive behavior, 123; of nest and young, 162; of territory, 86, 120, 125, 128-129, 134-135, 138; by threatening behavior, 123, 134-135; use of beak, 76; use of feet, 38
Determinate egg-layers, 144
Diatryma, 11
Dice, L.R., 62
Dinornis (moa), 12
Dinosaurs, 11, 17
Dipper, 119
Diseases of birds, 169, 170
Distribution of birds, 9, 17, 57, 81-83; biome pattern, 80-81; birdless regions, 85; Eurasia and North America, *map* 90-91; incongruities, 81-82; "life zone" concept, 80; Sclater's zoogeographical system, 79-80; shifts of range, 88. *See also* Populations
Diving birds, 13, 66-67. *See also* Booby; Gannet; Grebe; Loon; Pelican
Dodo, 26, 170, *180*
Domestication, 165-167. *See also* Fowl, domestic
Dove: mourning, *157;* nests, 140, *157;* rock, 167; turtle, 99; white-faced quail, feeding young, *159*
Dovekie, 83
Down feathers, 34, *53*
Drinking, mechanics of, 15, 26
Duck, 14, 62, 126; binocular vision to rear, 36; black-headed, 143; breeding age, 139; classification, 14, 20; domestic, 166, 169; evolution, 11; feet, *38;* fertility, 142; flight, *44-45;* flight muscles, 49; flight speed, 104; hunting of, 166, 168; incubation, 144; Labrador, *170;* mandarin, *18;* migration, 104; molting, 35, 54; nesting habits, 140, 145, 146; parasitism among, 143; pintail, banding, 115; pintail, Egyptian mural, *174;* redhead, 143; ruddy, eggs of, 142, ruddy, oil-spill victims, *177;* whistling; 148, 162. *See also* Brant; Canvasback; Eider; Mallard; Merganser; Scoter; Shoveler; Wigeon
Dunnock, 153
Dyeing of birds for tracking purposes, 109, 115, *116-117*

Eagle, 62, 63, 70; African hawk, 71; bald, 34, 64, 139, 171, 172, 179; classification, 20, 22; as deity, 174; eggs, 142; eye, 35, *51;* feeding of young, *146;* flight, 40; golden, 34, 138; monkey-eating, 63, 71; nests, 139; Pallas' sea, *51;* wing and tail design, 40; wing bone, *47*
Egg tooth, 9, 146
Eggs, *154-155;* color and marking, 143, 155; development synchronized by embryonic communication, 126; domestic fowl laying record, 144; effect of DDT on, 172, 179; embryonic development, 145, *150-151;* hatching, 146; incubation, 144-146; number laid by various species, 142, 144; of parasitic birds, 142, 143-144; question of recognition and retrieval by parents, 143; shapes, 142, 155; sizes, 13, 142, 146, 155; time and rate of laying, 142
Egret, *48,* 49; cattle, 58, *75,* 88; egg of snowy, *154; great, 130-131;* snowy, 172
Eider, 61, 162
Elephant bird, 12-13; egg, *154-155;* thigh bone, *41*
Embryonic development, 145, *150-151;* and imprinting, 126; synchronization, 126
Emlen, Stephen, 107-108
Emu, 13; classification, 13, 16, 20; egg, *154;* flightlessness, 12
Encephalitis, 169
Environment, 57; adaptation to, 11-12, 14, 171; climate, 80, 89; effect of man on, 81, 86, 167-172, 182-183; habitats, 57-58; landscape units, 80-81, *82-83;* range of, 9, 17, 88 (*see also* Distribution of birds)
Eocene, 11, 58
Europe: birdbanding in, 102-103; bird censuses, 84, 86, *map* 91; bird watching and protection, 171-172, *184*
Evolution of birds, 10-12; adaptive radiation (divergence), 11-12, 16; ancestral bird, *8,* 10; convergent, 13, 15, 16, 37; and extinction, 169, 170; feathers, 34; flight, 10, 40; flightless birds, 12; highest evolved birds, 16, 31; modern orders, 11; outlook, 169-170; from reptiles, 10, 17, 34, 35; of seed-eaters, 59; "true birds," 10
Extinction, 11, 169-171; actual, since 1600, 170; average evolutionary rate, 170; current threats, 15, 23, 85-86, 168, 169, 170, 172, 179, 182-183; man-induced, 84, 168, 169, 170, 180
Eyelids, 36; third (nictitans), 36, *50-51*
Eyes, 35, *50-51*
Eyesight, 35-37, 51; of birds of prey, 22, *35,* 51; monocular and binocular, 35, *diagrams* 36

Falcon, 62; beak, 71; Egyptian deity, 174; kestrel, 58, 62; peregrine, 62, *179,* 180; Falconets, 71
Falconiformes, *19,* 20, 22. *See also* Condor; Eagle; Falcon; Hawk; Osprey; Vulture
Falconry, 62, 101
Families. *See* Classification
Farrand, John, Jr., 20
Feathers: alula, *42;* coloring of, *52;* contour, 34, *53;* as currency, *176-177;* design and properties of, 33, *34;* down, 34, *53;* evolution of, 34; filoplumes, 34, *53;* finery, 34, 35, *52;* flight (quill), *13,* 33, *34,* 35, *53;* functions of, 34, 53; most distinctive characteristic of birds, 9-10; number of, in various species, 34, 53; owl wing, *53;* powderdown, 34; preening of, 54, *55;* primary, *13,* 39, 42, 44-45; tail, 13, 35, 53. *See also* Plumage
Feeding devices and behavior, 58-64, *65-77;* birds of prey, 14, 15, *22,* 62-63, 71, *76;* catching fish, *61,* 66-67, 77; cooperation *vs.* competition, 123; food calls, 122, 123, 126; nectar and fruit feeders, *15,* 59-60; piratical birds, 64; pouches, 14; scavenging, 57, *74-75;* securing food by association with other animals, 58, 64, *74-75;* seed-eaters, 59, *60, 76;* tongue adaptations, 58, *59,* 60, *68;* tool-using finch, 58-59; various bill adaptations, 12, 14, 15, 37, *59-61,* 68, *76-77;* woodpecker family, 58, *59, 68;* of young, 123, *125,* 126, *136,* 145, 146
Feet: scales on, 34; uses of, 37, 38. *See also* Foot adaptations
Fertility, 83, 142; determinate *vs.* indeterminate laying, 144
Fertilizer, guano, 61, *95,* 167-168
Fieldfare, 88
Filoplumes, 34, 53
Finches: abundance, 169; bill of seed-eating, 59; Galápagos, 11-12; highly evolved, 16, 31; weaver, 85; woodpecker (Galápagos), 58-59. *See also* Chaffinch; Goldfinch
Finland, bird censuses, 84, 86
Fish, as food source, 61, 89, 172
Fisher, James, 82, 83, 137, 170
Flamingo, 14, *55;* bill, 14, 37, *61;* classification, 14, 20; colonies, 85, *96-97;* diet, 57; fossil of primitive, 10; lesser, 57, 85; nests, 140
Flicker, fertility, 144
Flight: aerodynamics of, 39-40, *diagrams* 42-45; altitudes, 104; backward, 39, 44; of birds *vs.* other animals, 33; endurance, 25; evolution of, 10, 40; flapping, up-and-down-stroke, 39, *42,* 44-45; gliding, 40, *diagram* 43; hovering, 39, *44-45;* landing, 40; soaring, 40, *diagrams* 43; speeds, 15, 104
Flight adaptations, 41; air sacs, 35, 47, 49; bone structure, 35, *47;* keeled breastbone, 35, *46,* 47; musculature, 35, 47, 49; plumage, 33-34, *52-53;* shift of center of balance, 38; skeleton, *13,* 35, *46,* 47; vision, 35-37, 51; wings, *13,* 38-39, *42,* 43, 44
Flight (quill) feathers, *13,* 33, *34,* 35, *53*
Flightless birds: evolution of, 12; ratites, 12-13. *See also* Cassowary; Cormorant; Emu; Kiwi; Ostrich; Penguin; Rhea
Flycatcher, 20; ash-throated, 81; backward flight, 39; Coues, 81; Wied's crested, 81; distribution, altitudinal zones, *81;* nests, 140; olivaceous, 81; song of, 121; tyrant, 122;

vermilion, 81; western, 81
Flying reptiles, 10
"Flyways," *maps* 102-103, 104
Food: of birds of prey, 62-63, 104; fish, 61, 89, 172; fruit, 60; insects, 58, 87, 170; intake, 58, graph 62; nectar, 16, 59-60; plankton, 60-61; plant, 59; seeds, 59; storing, *65;* versatility of most birds, *64, 65;* of young birds, 59, 146. *See also* Feeding devices and behavior
Foot adaptations, 37-38; for attack and defense, 38; classification by, 16; hooked talons of birds of prey, 14, 15, *22, 38,* 71; lobe and paddle-footed swimmers, 13, 23, *38;* long toes of marsh waders, 37-38, *39;* "snowshoes" of grouse, 38, *39;* syndactyl feet, 16; toe-locking device of perching birds, *37,* 38; toes for scratching, 15, 22, *39;* two back toes for bracing against tree trunks, *38,* 58; two-toed ostrich, 13, *39;* for walking, *39;* web-footed swimmers, 14, *38*
Fossilization of birds, 11
Fossils: *Archaeopteryx, 8,* 10; birds known from, *10-11; Hesperornis,* 10; *Ichthyornis,* 10; primitive flamingo, 10
Fowl, domestic, 15, *164,* 165-167; chicken, 123, 165-166; duck, 166; fertility, 144, 166; spurs, 38; transmission of encephalitis by, 169; turkey, *164,* 166-167
Fowl-like birds, 14-15, *22;* arena behavior, 124-125; evolution of, 11. *See also* Grouse; Hoatzin; Jungle fowl; Mallee fowl; Partridge; Pheasant; Ptarmigan; Quail; Scrub fowl
Friedmann, Herbert, 64
Frigate bird, 14, 60; classification, 14, 20; pirates, 64; skeleton, 47; wing design, 40
Frings, Hubert and Mabel, 123
Frisch, Johann Leonhard, 101
Frith, H.J., 146
Frogmouth, 20; tawny, *28*
Fruiteaters, 60
Fulmar, 20; northern, 83

Galápagos finches, 11-12, 58
Galápagos Islands, 11, 86
Galápagos penguin, 86, 92
Galliformes, *18,* 20, *22. See also* Fowl-like birds
Game birds: exploitation, 85, 168; fertility, 142, 168; surveys, 86; transplantation, 88
Gannet, 66, 124; eggs, 142; feet, 38; incubation, 145
Garuda, bird deity, 174
Gaviiformes, *19,* 20. *See also* Loon
Geese. *See* Goose
Geologic Time Scale, *table* 14
Germany, navigation studies, 107
Gliding, 40, *diagram* 43; wing shape for, *42*
Goatsuckers, 15. *See also*

189

Index, continued

Nighthawk; Nightjar; Whippoorwill
Goldcrest, egg clutch of, 142
Goldfinch, 34, 104, 140
Goose, 14, 62, 126, 177; banding, *115;* blue, 104; Canada, *78,* 123; classification, 14, 20; dyeing of, for tracking, 116; feet, 38; flight, 40, 104; flight muscles, 49; graylag, 126; Hawaiian (néné), *87;* hunting of, 168; incubation, 144; migration, 104, 106; molting, 35, 54; Ross's, 106; snow, *115*
Goshawk, 22, 63, 64, 88
Gould, John, *167*
Grackle, 68, 169, 171; migration, 104
Great Britain, bird populations, 84, 86, 171
Grebe, 13, 61; classification, 13, 16, 20; defense of young, 162; feet, 13, *38;* floating nest, 140, *147;* great crested, *19;* horned, *17, 38;* red-necked, *147;* western, courtship ritual, *132-133;* western, oil-spill victims, *176-177*
Greenewalt, Crawford, 39, 59
Griffiths, Alex, 60
Grinnell, Joseph, 123
Grosbeak, 123; evening, *98;* pine, 87
Groups of birds, terms for, *table* 169
Grouse, 119, 146, 168; black, 125; classification, 14, 20, 24; courtship behavior, *118,* 125; defense of young, 162; feet, 38, *39;* incubation, 144; population cycles, 87; red, 87; ruffed, *39,* 87, 88, *118;* sage, 125; sharptail, 125. *See also* Ptarmigan
Gruiformes, *19,* 20, *23;* decimation of, 23, 169. *See also* Bustard; Coot; Crane; Rail
Guacharo. *See* Oilbird
Guano birds, off Peru, 61, 84, *94-95,* 167-168
Guans, 15
Guillemot, 126
Gull, 15, 60, 64, 143; blackheaded, 120; classification, 15, 20, 24; dyeing of, for tracking, *116-117;* eggs, 142; feeding instinct, *125,* 126; feeding of young, 159; feet, 38; herring, *116-117,* 123, *125,* 126, 139, 143; kittiwake, 61, *92;* laughing, 64; scavengers, 57, *74-75;* skeleton, *46;* wing design, 40, 43

Halcyon, 140. *See also* Kingfisher
Hawk, 62-63, 70, 123, 179; accipiters, 62; banding, 101; beak, 15, 22, 37; classification, 15, 16, 20, 22; eggs, 142; eyesight, 22, *35,* 36, 51; feet and talons, 15, 22, 38; flight, 40, *diagram* 43, 104; food intake, *graph* 62; goshawk, *22,* 63, 64, 88; incubation, 144-145; redshouldered, 62; red-tailed, 40, 62, *72-73;* rough-legged, *42,* 87; sharpshin, 63; sparrow, 63; tail design, 40; wing design, 40, *42. See also* Osprey
Heath hen, extinct, 170, *171*
Hell-diver. *See* Grebe
"Helper" birds, 145
Heron, 14, 61, 119; bill, 37; classification, 14, 20; courtship, 124; evolution, 11; feet, 37, *39;* great blue, *39;* incubation, 144-145; nesting grounds, 141; night, 124, 143; white, 88
Hesperornis, 10
Hibernation, 99-100
Hickey, Joseph J., 172
Hoatzin, eye, *51*
Hoffmann, Klaus, 107
Hole nesters, 16, 29, 140, 143
Homing ability, 106, 108; study of, *111*
Honey creeper, Hawaiian, 60, 170
Honey guide, 20, 64, 74; greater, 64; parasitism of, 143, *152*
Hoopoe, 16, 20; long-beaked, *29*
Hornbill, 16, 20, 29; beak, 37, *76;* eye, *50;* female, molting, 35, 54; ground, *50,* 58; rufous, *76*
Horus, bird deity, 174
Hovering flight, 39, *44-45*
Huia, 37
Hummingbird, 16, 20; arena behavior, 125; bee, 59; bills, *15;* broad-billed, egg of, *155;* eggs, 142, *155;* feet, 38; fertility, 142; flight, 39, *43, 44-45,* 59-60; flight muscles, 35; hermit, *15;* metabolism, 59; nectar-feeding, 16, 59-60; nests, 139; number of feathers, 34; ruby-throated, 34, 39, 59; sicklebill, *15;* skeleton, *41;* swordbill, *15;* thornbill, *15;* torpor of, 100; wing-beat rate, 39, 48; wing design, 39, 43, 44
Hunting, 166, 168, 180; birds made extinct by, *170-171,* 180, *181;* Egyptian mural, *174. See also* Game birds
Huxley, Thomas H., 9

Ibis, 14, 61; glossy, *19,* 143
Ice ages, 11
Ichthyornis, 10
Imprinting, 126, 144
Incubation, 144-146
Indeterminate egg-layers, 144
Insecticides, effect on birds, 84, 172, 179, 184
Insects: comparison of birds with, 33, 39; control by birds, 87; as food source, 58, 87, 170
International Union for the Conservation of Nature and Natural Resources, 170

Jacamar, 16, 20
Jacana, 20; northern, egg, *155;* pheasant-tailed, *18;* toes, 38
Jaeger, 64
Jaeger, Edmund C., 100
Japan, 112; breeding, 166; conservation, 172
Jay, 64, 68, 145; blue, 104, 171; highly evolved, 16, 31; migration, 104
Junco, song of, 121
Jungle fowl, red, *22,* 165, 167
Jurassic, 10

Keeton, William, 108
Kendeigh, S. Charles, 87, 138
Kestrel, 58, *62;* vision, 35
Killdeer, 121, *145*
Kingbird, 171
Kingfisher, 16, 119; bill, 16, 37; classification, 16, 20, 29; eggs, 143; nest, 140, 157
Kinglet, 123; egg clutch, 142
Kite, 63; Everglade, 63, 85; swallow-tailed, 88
Kittiwake, 61, *92*
Kiwi, 13; brown, *18;* brown, egg of, *155;* classification, 13, 20; flightlessness, 12; incubation, 145; sense of sight and smell, 36
Knot, *89*
Kramer, Gustav, 106, 107, 111

Lack, David, 104, 120, 138
Land birds, 15-16, 31; breeding age, 83; colonial, 84, 85, 138; flight altitude, 104; migration, 100-101, 102, 103, 104; nesting densities, 84-85; ocean crossings, 88, 100, 102-103, 105; territory, 86-87, *128-129,* 137-138, 139
Landing action, 40
Lapwing, 88; crowned, *75*
Lark, 20, 99; horned, habitat, 81; migration, 104; toes, 38; wood, 104. *See also* Skylark
Lawrence, Louise de Kiriline, 121
Learning, 119; song, 121
Legs, *37,* 38; scales on, 34
"Life zones," Merriam's system of, 80, 82
Lightness of birds: air sac system, 35, 47; feathers, 33; hollow bones, 35, *47*
Linnaeus, 100
Lizard skeleton, compared to bird, *12-13*
Locust bird, 85
Loon, 13, 61; arctic, *19;* bill, 37; classification, 13, 16, 20; diving, 66; eyesight, 35; feet, 13, 38; red-necked, nest of, 156
Lorenz, Konrad, 126
Lorikeet, 20, 60; rainbow, *26-27,* 60
Lory, 20
Lovebird, 20
Lowery, George H., Jr., 103
Lungs, 35, 49
Lyrebird, 16, 31, *135, 161*

Macaw, 20, 26; blue-and-yellow, *19*
Maleo, 146
Mallard, 166; feet, *38*
Mallee fowl, 142, *143,* 145-146
Mammals, 10; Age of, 11; bird associations with, 58, 64, *74-75;* comparisons with birds, 33, 35, 39
Manakin, arena behavior, 125
Manucode. *See* Bird of paradise
Marabou, 63
Marco Polo, 12
Martin: house, nest of, 140; purple, 171
Mating, 139; in colonies, 92; loyalty rites after, 124, 148. *See also* Courtship
Mayfield, Harold, 86
Meadowlark, 121, 138, *144,* 171; habitat, *82;* song notations, *120*
Megapode (mound builder), 15, 140; egg of, *154. See also* Mallee fowl; Scrub fowl
Merganser, 14, 62
Merikalio, Einari, 84
Merriam, Clinton Hart, 80
Metabolism, 35, 49; of hummingbird, 59. *See also* Body heat
Migration, 100-108; causes and timing, 100-101, 104-105; definitions, 100; distances, 102, 107; diurnal, 103-104, *diagram* 106, 107; flight altitude, 104; flight speed, 104; flyways and routes, *maps* 102-103, 104; hazards of, 101, 105; history of theories of, 99-100; homing ability, 106, 108, *111;* nocturnal, 103, 104, 106, *diagram* 107, 108, 122; number of birds engaged in, 100; partial, 104; reasons for, 100, 105; tracking, 109, *112-115,* 116 (*see also* Banding; Radar tracking); transoceanic, of land birds, 100, 102-103, 105; voice contact, 122-123. *See also* Navigation
Miocene, 11, 59
Moa, 12
Mockingbird, 171; song, 121; wingbeat, 39
Molting, 34-35, *54*
Morony, John J., 20
Motmot, 16, 20
Mound builder, 15, 140. *See also* Mallee fowl; Scrub fowl
Mousebird, 16, 20; whiteheaded, *19*
Murre: colony, *92;* common, 61; egg, 142, *154,* 155; thick-billed, 61
Musculature, flight, 35, 47, 49
Mutton bird, 171
Mutualism, cases of, 64, 74, *75*
Myna bird, 121
Mythology, birds in, 174

National Audubon Society, 82
Natural History of Birds, Buffon, 166
Natural selection, 58, 59, 64; aided by birds of prey, 63
Navigation, 101, 104, 105-108, 111, 112; celestial, *diagrams* 106-107, 108, 111, 112; diurnal, *diagram* 106, 107; experiments, 107-108, *110-115;* homing ability, 106, 108, *111;* magnetic direction finding, 108, 112; by memory, 106, 111, 112; nocturnal, *diagram* 107, 108; theories on, 106-107, 108, 111, 112
Nectar-feeding birds, 16, 59-60, 170
Néné, *87*
Neornithes, 10
Nest building, 139-142, 145, 157; evolution of, 139; instinct, 142
Nesting ground density of colonial birds, 84, 85, 138, 140-142
Nests, 139-141, *156-157;* communal, 141-142; hanging, *140,* 141, *156;* holes, 16, 29, 140; in or near insect nests, 140, 141; mounds, 140, *143;* mud, 140, *141;* open-topped bowls, 140, *157;* protection of, 162; sizes, 139; tunnels, 140
Newman, Robert J., 103
Nictitans, third eyelid, 36, *50-51*
Nighthawk, 15, 29, 38, 100, 171
Nightjar, 20, 29, 64, 119, 121, 139; pennant-winged, *19*
Nocturnal birds, 15, 29, 36, 62
North America: birdbanding program, 101; bird population, 82, *map* 90; bird protection, 168, 171, 172, 183, 184; "flyways" of, 103; most numerous bird, 85; rare birds, 85, *86-87,* 170; recently extinct birds, *170-171,* 184. *See also* United States
Notornis, 170

Nutcracker, beak, 68
Nuthatch, 58, 123; pygmy, 162

Ocean crossings by land birds, 88, 100, 102-103, 105
Oil spills, damage to birds, *176-177*
Oilbird, 29, 64
Oligocene, 11
Onagadori, 166
Orders. *See* Classification
Origin of Species, Darwin, 10
Oriole, 171; Baltimore, 172; egg of northern, *154;* nests, 139, 140; northern, 59, *129*
Ornithosis, 169
Oropendola, nest of, 140-141
Osprey, 40, 64, 66, 172; foot, *38*
Ostrich, 12, 13, *18, 75,* 169; classification, 13, 16, 20; egg, 142; evolution, 11; flightlessness, 12; foot, 13, 38, *39;* size of eyes, 35; stone age mural, *173*
Ovenbird, rufous, nest of, 140, *141,* 156
Owl, 15, 62; Asiatic fishing, *50;* barn, 62, 145; barred, 62; classification, 14, 15, 16, 20; eggs, 142, 143, *154;* evolution, 11; eyes and vision, 15, 35, *diagram* 36, *50,* 62, 70; feet and talons, 15, 38, 71; great horned, 62, *70-71,* 154, *178;* hearing, 70; incubation, 144-145; long-eared, 62; mobility of neck, 36, *56;* mythical wisdom, Greek depiction, *174;* saw-whet, 36; short-eared, *56,* 88; skull, *47;* snowy, 87-88; spectacled, *18;* wing feathers, *53*
Oxpecker, red-billed, 74, *75*
Oystercatcher, 115; bill, *60*

Paleocene, 11
Parakeet, 20; beak, *76;* Carolina, extinct, 170, *171;* monk, 142; as pet, 167
Parasitic birds, 143-144, *152-153*
Parental care, *162-163;* cleaning of nest, 146, *161;* defense of nest and young, 162; feeding of young, 126, 146, *147, 158-160;* "helper" birds, 145; incubation of eggs, 144-145; rituals, *130-131*
Parrot, 15, 38, 60; beak, 15, 37, 68; classification, 15, 20, 26; eggs, 143; food call, 60; incubation, 144-145
Partridge, 13, 15
Passeriformes, *19,* 20, *30-31. See also* Perching birds; and families like Finch; Sparrow; Warbler; etc.
Passerines. *See* Perching birds
Peacock, plumage, *52,* 148
Pelecaniformes, *19,* 20, 169. *See also* Anhinga; Booby; Cormorant; Frigate bird; Pelican; Tropic bird
Pelican, 14, 60, 61; beak, 37; brown, *19,* 64, *66-67, 158-159;* classification, 14, 16, 20; egg of white, *155;* evolution, 11; flight, 40; wingbeat, 39
Penguin, 13-14; Adélie, 83, 122; classification, 20; colonies, 83, 92, *93;* emperor, *162;* flightlessness, 12, 13, 15; Galápagos, 86, 92; king, eye of, *51;* Magellanic, *93;* molting, 54; nurseries, 92, *162;* rockhopper, *18*
Perching birds, 16, 30-31; ascendancy of, 16, 169-170; breeding, 142, 144, 145; feeding of young, 159, *160;* seed-eating, 59, 169-170; toe-locking device of, *37,* 38
Peregrine falcon, 62, *179,* 180
Peru, guano birds off coast of, 61, 84, *94-95,* 167-168
Pesticides. *See* Insecticides
Peterson, Roger Tory, 90
Petrel, 14, 20, 36; abundance of, 83; fertility, 83, 142; storm, 14, 83; Wilson's, 83, 101
Pets, birds as, 167
Pettingill, Olin Sewall, 119
Phalarope, feet of, 38
Pheasant, 15, 38, 148, 165, 168; argus, arena behavior, 125; classification, 15, 20; fertility, 142; golden, *18;* transmission of encephalitis, 169; wing design, 42
Phoebe, 101, 146, 171
Phorusrhacids, 11
Phorusrhacos, 11
Photoperiodism, 105
Piciformes, *18,* 20. *See also* Barbet; Honey guide; Jacamar; Toucan; Woodpecker
Pigeon, 15, 33; carrier, homing experiment, *111;* classification, 15, 20, 26; domestic, 167; eye, *50;* gliding ability, *43;* homing ability, 106, 108; as message bearer, 167; navigation studies, 106, 108, *114;* passenger, extinct, 170, 171, 180, *181, 182;* pintail green, *18;* transmitter of ornithosis, 169; Victoria crowned, *26, 50;* wing design, 43; wingbeat, 39
"Pigeon milk," 59, 159
Pigeon racing, 167
Piper. *See* Sandpiper
Pipit, 38, 153; meadow, 144; tree, 152
Piquero, 61, 95
Piratical birds, 64
Plankton, as food, 60-61
Pleistocene, 11, 169, 170
Pliocene, 11, 169
Plover, 61; classification, 20, 24; golden, migration of, 25, 100, 102, 107; killdeer, 121; *145;* lapwing, *75.* 88
Plumage: body heat regulation by, *34,* 53; courtship, 35, 120-124, 125, 148; "eclipse," 54; fluffing of, 120, 125; molting, 34-35, *54. See also* Feathers
Plymouth Rock hen, 34
Podicipediformes, *19,* 20. *See also* Grebe
Poorwill, hibernation of, 100
Populations of birds: censuses, 84-85, 86; cyclic patterns of density, 87-88; decimation by pesticides, 84, 172, 179; densities, 84-85, 95; domestic chicken, 165; estimated total, 82; estimated U.S. land birds, 82, 84; Eurasia and North America, map 90-91; explosions, 169-170; man-made control of, 168-169; natural control of, 86-87; sea birds, 82-84, 95
Posner, Gerald, 61

Potoo, 29
Pouches, throat, 14
Poultry raising, *164,* 166-167
Powder-down feathers, 34
Prairie chicken, 125, 170
Precocial birds, 144, *145,* 146
Predators. *See* Birds of prey
Primary feathers, *13,* 39, 42, 44-45
Procellariiformes, *18-19,* 20. *See also* Albatross; Fulmar; Petrel
Protection of birds by man, 168, 171-172, *179,* 183, *184-185*
Protective devices. *See* Defense
Psittaciformes, *19,* 20, *26-27. See also* Cockatoo; Lorikeet; Parakeet; Parrot
Psittacosis, 169
Ptarmigan, 74; eggs, 143; rock, molting, *54;* willow, 87, 100
Pterodactyls, 10
Pterosaurs, 11
Puffbird, 20
Puffin, 16, 24, 61, 83-84, 134

Quail, 15, 146, 168; bobwhite, *49,* 121, 122, 126; classification, 15, 20
Quelea, 85
Quetzal, northern, *18*
Quill (flight) feathers, *13,* 33, *34,* 35, *53*

Radar tracking, 108, 109, *112-113,* 115
Rail, 15, 20, 23, 119, 169
Ratites, 12-13, 169
Raven, 31, 81-82; foot, *39*
Redpoll, 87
Redstart, 99, 144; habitat, 81, *83*
Reference List of the Birds of the World (Morony, Bock, Farrand), 20
Regurgitation, 159
"Releasers," 120
Religion, birds in, 174
Reproduction: breeding age, 83, 139; fertility, 83, 142. *See also* Courtship; Eggs; Mating
Reptiles: Age of, 11; ascendancy of birds over, 11; bird skeleton compared to, *12-13;* evolution of birds from, 10, 17, 34, 35; flying, 10; similarities with birds, 9, 146
Respiratory system, 35, 49
Rhea, 13; classification, 13, 16, 20; flightlessness, 12; greater, *18*
Rheiformes, *18,* 20. *See also* Rhea
"Ringing." *See* Banding of birds
Robin, 64, 126, 138; abundance of, 85, 171; American, 36, 85, 88, 104, *128,* 129, 140; danger of pesticides to, 172; defense of territory, 86, 120, *128-129,* 138; egg of American, *155;* European, 99, 138; food call, 123; migration, 104; nest, 140; red-breast, 120; size of territory, 138
Roc, 12-13
Rock dove, 167
Roller, 16, 20; diet, 58; lilac-breasted, *19*
Ruff, courtship plumage, 125-126

Sandgrouse, 15, 20
Sandpiper, 61; Baird's, 102; buff-breasted, 102-103; classification, 16, 20, 24; incubation, 145; migration, 102, map 103; pectoral, 102, *103;* white-rumped, 102. *See also* Ruff: Yellowlegs
Sauer, E.F.G., 107, 111
Saunders, Aretas A., 120
Scales, on feet and legs, 34
Scavengers, 57. *See also* Gull; Vulture
Sclater, P.L., 79-80
Scoter, 61, 62
Scott, John, 125
Screamer, 20
Scrub bird, 170
Scrub fowl: egg, *154;* nest, 140
Sea birds: breeding age, 83, 139; colonies, 83-84, 85, 89, *92-95,* 138; distribution, 60-61, 89; feeding of young, *158-159;* food sources, 60-61, 89; migration, 101; number of species, 60; populations, 82-84, 85, 89
Secretary bird, 11, 63
Seedeaters, 59; bill, *60, 76;* population explosions, 169-170
Selective breeding, 166, 167
Sense organs, 36-37. *See also* Eyes
Sexual maturity, age of, 83, 139
Sharptail, 125
Shearwater, 14, 36, 83; greater, 101; homing ability, 106; Manx, 106; migration, 101; short-tailed, 83, 101; sooty, 101; wing design, 42
Shoebill, beak, *76*
Shore birds, wading, 15, 24-25, 61; evolution of, 11; flight speed, 104; migration, 100, 102-103; removal from game list; 85, 168. *See also* Curlew; Oystercatcher; Plover: Sandpiper; Snipe
Shoveler, 62
Shrike, northern, *65,* 87
Sibley, C. G., 14
Sight, sense of. *See* Eyesight
Simon, James, 125
Singing. *See* Song
Skeletal structure, *41, 46;* adaptation for flight, *13,* 35, 47
Skimmer, black, 24, 76, *77;* egg of, *154*
Skua, 24, 64
Skull, 37, *47*
Skylark: courtship flight, 148; migration, 104; song, 121
Sleeping sickness, 169, 170
Smell, sense of, 36-37
Snakebird. *See* Anhinga
Snipe, 61, 119; egg of common, *154;* sense of smell, 36
Soaring flight, 40, *diagrams* 43; wing shapes for, 40, *42,* 43
Social behavior, 119; loyalty rites after mating, 124, 148. *See also* Colonial birds; Communication
Solenhofen fossil, 10
Solitary birds, 119; densities, 84; territory of, 86-87, *128-129,* 137-139
Song, 119-122; courtship, 120, 122, 128, 148; for defense of territory, 86, 120, 128, 134, 137; definition, 119; dialects, 121-122; forms of notation, *120;* functions of, 120, 122; identification by, 121, 148; individual variations, 122; learning, 121; mimicry, 121; tape recorder studies, *120,* 122, 123
Songbirds, 20; banding, 115; breeding age, 139; number of feathers, 34; sizes of territory,

Index, continued

138; vision, *diagram* 36
Sound: bird names derived from, *table* 121; functions, 122, 134, 135; production, 119, 124. *See also* Communication; Song
Sparrow, 74, 148, *153;* abundance of, 85, 169; chipping, 171; classification, 16, 20; gliding ability, *43;* highly evolved, 16, 31; house, 34, 53, 85, 88; number of feathers, 34, 53; song, *82, 127,* 138, 140, 144, 171; songs of, 121-122; vision, *diagram* 36; white-crowned, *36,* 121-122; white-throated, 103
Species: defined, 12; "good," 171
Species of birds, number of: estimated total, extant and extinct, 11; extant, 11, 12, 17, 20; extinct known from fossils, 11; perching birds, 16; sea birds, 60; song dialects of, and subspecies development, 121-122
Sphenisciformes, *18,* 20. *See also* Penguin
Spine, 35, *46*
Spoonbill, 37, 61, 159; roseate, *130-131*
Spurs, 38
Stager, Kenneth, 37
Starling, *30-31;* abundance of, 85; classification, 30; flight speed, 104; migration, 104; navigation studies, *diagrams* 106, 107, *110;* as song mimic, 121; transplantation, 88
Stilt, 20
Stork, 14, 61, 99; Algerian white, 184; classification, 14, 20; communication, 124; European white, *102,* 124; feeding of young, 159; incubation, 144-145; migration, *map* 102; protection in Europe, *184. See also* Marabou
Streamertail, *19*
Strigiformes, *18,* 20. *See also* Owl
Struthioniformes, *18,* 20. *See also* Ostrich
Sunbird, 59-60
Swallow, 99, 101, 138, 171; bank, 171; barn, 102, 171; classification, 20; cliff, 140, 162, 171; diet, 58; feet, 38; flight, 40, 104; migration, 102, 104; nests, 140, 157; tree, 171; wing design, *42*
Swan, 14, 62; care of young, *162-163;* classification, 14, 20; migration, 104; mute, *21;* trumpeter, 88; whistling, number of feathers, 34
Swift, 15, 171; beak, 15, 38; chimney, 141; classification, 15-16, 20; colonial, 138; crested tree, 139; diet, 58; eggs, 143; European, 100, 106; eyesight, 51;

feet, 15, 38; flight speed, 15; homing ability, 106; nests, 139, 141, 156; palm, 141; swallow-tailed, 141; torpor of, 100; white-throated, 100; wing action, 39
Swiftlet, cave, nest of, 141
Swimmers: feet of, *38;* "totipalmate," 14; "tube-nosed," 14; waterfowl, 14, 31
Systema Naturae, Linnaeus, 100

Tail feathers, 13, 35, 53
Tailorbird, redheaded, *156-157*
Tanager, 122
Tanner, James, 138
Teeth: absence of, 37; egg tooth, 9, 146; present in ichthyornis, 10
Tern, 15, *32,* 60, 64; arctic, *102,* 103, 156; bill, 37; classification, 15, 20, 24; colonies, 83, 85; courtship, 123-124; defense of young, 162; elegant, 85, 138; fertility, 83; incubation, 145; migration, *map* 102; molting, *54;* nesting grounds, 85, 138, 141; nests of, 139, *156;* royal, *24-25;* sooty, 83, 143; white (fairy), classification, *table* 16
Territory of individual birds, 86-87, *128-129,* 138-139; defense of, 120, 125, 128, *134-135,* 138; establishment of, 137-138; sizes, 138
Thecodonts, 10
Thrasher, brown, song of, 120
Thrush, 20; European song, nest of, 140; ocean crossings, 103; song of, 120, 122. *See also* Bluebird; Robin
Tick bird, African, 74
Tinamiformes, *18,* 20. *See also* Tinamou
Tinamou, 13, 20; elegant-crested, *18;* elegant-created, egg of, *155*
Tinbergen, Niko, 120, 125, 146
Tit: blue, 142; bush, 123; eggs, 142; great, feeding of young, 146; long-tailed, 142
Titmouse, 123; tufted, 88; nests, 140. *See also* Chickadee
Tody, 16, 20
Tongue adaptations, 58, *59,* 60, *68*
Tool-using finch, 58-59
Torpidity, 100
Totipalmate swimmers, 14
Toucan, 16, 20; ariel, *76;* beak, 37, *76;* eggs, 142; red-breasted, *18*
Touraco, 15, 20; red-crested, *19;* white-cheeked, *27*
Trogon, 16, 20
Trogoniformes, *18,* 20
Tropic bird, 20, 83
Tropics, birds of: density, 84;

variety, 89
Troupial, nest of, 139
Tube-nosed swimmers, 14
Turkey, 15; classification, 14-15, 20, 22; domesticated, *164,* 166-167; embryonic development, *150-151;* wild; arena behavior, 124
Turnstone, 104

United States: bird protection, 168, 171, 172, 183; estimated bird population, 82; most numerous bird, 85; population densities, 84; poultry raising, 166. *See also* North America
U.S. Fish and Wildlife Service, 86, 115, 168

Vireo, 58, 122; nests, 140; red-eyed, 81, 121, 144; song, 121
Vision. *See* Eyesight
Vogt, William, 120
Vulture, 14, 57, 62, 63; beak, *76;* black, 37, 63; classification, 14, 20; cleanliness of, 63; eye, *51;* eyesight, 35, 37; flight and landing, 40; king, *51, 76;* palm-nut, 64; sense of smell, 37; turkey, 37, 40; white-headed, *19;* wing and tail design, 40. *See also* Condor

Wading birds, long-legged, 14, 61; feet, 37-38, *39. See also* Egret; Flamingo; Heron; Ibis; Spoonbill; Stork
Wading shore birds. *See* Shore birds
Walcott, Charles, 108
Walking, 38; foot adaptations for, *39*
Walton, Izaak, 61
Warbler, 146, 153; backward flight, 39; bay-breasted, 87; blackpoll, 105, 106; black-throated green, 80, *160;* classification, 20; diet, 58; eyesight, 35; Kirtland's, 86, 144; leaf, 121; magnolia, 58; migration, 103, 105, 106, 122; navigation study, *diagrams* 107; nests, 140, 141; ocean crossings, 103, 105; pine, 121; reed, 121; rock, 141; sedge, 121; size of territory, 87; songs of, 121; willow, 144; wood, 58, 122; yellow, 171; yellowthroat, 120
Warning cries, 120, 123
Water birds, 31, 36, 61-62; evolution, 10
Waterfowl, 14; banding, 102; fertility, 168; hunting, 168; migration, 103, 106; molting, 35, 54; population and

protection, 168
Waxbill, 152
Waxwing, 60; Bohemian, 60, 87; cedar, 60; migration, 104
Weaverbird, 169; baya, 156; nests, 139, *140,* 141, *156;* sociable, 141-142; waxbill, 152
Weller, Milton, 143
Wetmore, Alexander, 34
Whippoorwill, 15, 38, 64, 139; classification, 15, 29; song, 121
Whydah, Jackson's dancing, 125
Widow bird, African, 152
Wigeon, 62, 64
Wilson, Alexander, *166,* 171
Windows, birds flying against, 86
Wing, Leonard, 82
Wing bone, *13, 47*
Wingbeat, rate of, 39, 48
Wings: flapping action of, 39, *42, 44-45;* functioning of, 39, *diagrams* 42-45; hovering action of, 39, *44-45;* landing action of, 40; largest size, 14, 40, *148;* structure and shapes of, *13,* 38-39, 40, *42,* 43, 44
Wood peewee, 121
Woodcock: bill, 37; binocular vision to rear, *diagram* 36; courtship flight, *148;* "song" of, 119
Woodcreeper, 58
Woodpecker, 16, 121, 123, 143; classification, 16, 20; eggs, 143; feeding, and adaptations for, 58, *59, 68;* foot, *38, 58;* great spotted, *68;* green, *68;* hairy, habitat, *83;* ivory-billed, 85, *86,* 138, 170, 171; nests, 140; pileated, 138, 171; red-bellied, 138; sizes of territory, 138; tapping of, 119
Woodpecker finch, 58-59
Wren: cactus, 80; Carolina, 88; classification, 16, 20; fertility, 142; house, 171; long-billed marsh, 140; nests, 140, 157
Wryneck, European, fertility, 144

Yellowhammer nestlings, *136*
Yellowlegs: lesser, 115; migration, 102
Yellowthroat, 120
Young birds: altricial, *144,* 146; born coldblooded, 162; care of (*see* Parental care); diet of, 59, 146; feeding of, 123, *125,* 126, 145, 146, *147, 158-159;* gape and mouth coloring, *136;* precocial, *145,* 146

Zoogeographical regions, Sclater's, 79-80